After the bitter struggle of World War II, Britain looked forward to many years of peace and happiness. However, events in Malaya, Korea and the Suez once more rocked the stability of peacetime Britain. Despite this, there were many occasions to give the nation a sense of pride. We've selected some events from the Golden Years of 1946–1956 that are still remembered today — although we are sure many readers will have their own personal memories.

The Coronation of Queen Elizabeth II
On June 2nd, 1953, over 8,000 guests, including Prime Ministers and Heads of State from around the world, witnessed the ceremony in Westminster Abbey. Thanks to the BBC's outside broadcast production, millions were also given the chance to watch this historic event on TV in the comfort of their own or a neighbour's home.

On the music side, Bill Haley and the Comets were just one of the many Rock 'n' Roll bands hitting the headlines. But the Golden Years were to see the emergence of a new superstar, Elvis Presley.

The Roof of the World

To conquer Everest, the highest mountain in the world, was every climber's dream. On May 29th, 1953, the team that reached the 29,028-foot summit was British-led, but it was a New Zealander and a Nepalese who achieved the ultimate mountaineering feat. Edmund Hillary and sherpa Tenzing Norgay were to become the most famous and most feted mountaineers of their generation.

The "Miracle Mile"

At Iffley Road Track, Oxford, on May 6th, 1954, three thousand spectators witnessed a piece of sporting history. Competing in the mile race was Roger Bannister, running for the Amateur Athletics Association against Oxford University. Bannister took the lead with 200 yards to go and sprinted to the tape, finishing in 3 minutes 59.4 seconds — the first-ever sub-four-minute mile.

And, slightly closer to home...

The winter of 1946-47 was described by many as being the worst in living memory. Huge blizzards cut off villages, and the whole country ground to a halt. Scotland was particularly badly affected. Our picture shows a train that had become stranded near Auchterhouse, Perthshire. Two hundred men were needed to dig it out of the snow.

Printed and Published in Great Britain by D. C. Thomson & Co., Ltd., 185 Fleet Street, London, EC4A 2HS. © D. C. Thomson & Co., Ltd., 2007   ISBN: 978 1 84535 327 8

6

The Sunday Post 14th April 1946

The Sunday Post 15th September 1946

The Sunday Post 2nd June 1946

The Sunday Post 8th December 1946

The Sunday Post 20th October 1946

1947

Mathematics, history, English, physics and geography were, no doubt, among Horace's favourite subjects at school. But when he wasn't doing his homework (which he would do every night without fail and without Maw nagging him!) he was likely to relax with one of his favourite comics. There were lots to choose from in 1947 and one of his favourites could well have been "Adventure".

Next Issue on Sale Tuesday, 16th Sept.

SEE INSIDE FOR NEW GREAT

Adventure

THE QUEST OF THE GOLDEN HAMMER

Varda the Wolf is dead and Erik the Viking is near the end of the search for the Golden Hammer. While Harvard the Hacker goes to release the imprisoned Vikings, captured by the Sultan of Majorca, the Sultan himself leads Erik to the Golden Hammer.

THE GOLDEN HAMMER WAS CLUTCHED IN AN IRON HAND ON TOP OF A PILLAR.

THE TREACHEROUS SULTAN HAD CHEATED THE VIKING LEADER.

WITH THE CLUTCHING HAND CLOSING EVER TIGHTER, HARVARD THE HACKER CAME TO THE RESCUE.

HE WAS JUST IN TIME ERIK FROM BEING TO DEATH.

HIS MIGHTY AXE MADE SHORT WORK OF THE PILLAR AND —

THE VIKINGS CHEERED AS ERIK WAVED THE SACRED TROPHY IN THE AIR.

THE QUEST OF THE GOLDEN HAMMER WAS ENDED AND THE VIKINGS SAILED FOR HOME.

Turn to Page 54 for news of a grand new picture-story!

THE QUEST OF THE GOLDEN HAMMER

Erik and his Vikings have tracked Varda the Wolf, stealer of the Golden Hammer, to the Island of Majorca. By a cunning trick, the Vikings are captured by the Sultan of Majorca and now Erik and Harvard the Hacker face death in the arena against two ferocious lions.

UNARMED, THE TWO VIKINGS BATTLED WITH THE MAN-

WITH A MIGHTY HEAVE, HE HURLED ROYAL BOX WHERE SAT THE SUI

— THE LION HAD KILLED VARDA AND THE SULTAN WAS IN DEADLY DANGER.

ALL ERIK'S STRENG THE BLOW WITH WHICH FELLED THE MAN-EA

The Prize-Fighter who ran away from his trainer!

TINKER COBB
THE BARE-FIST BATTLER

STARTING TO-DAY—

Boys could escape from schoolwork in the company of such characters as "Tinker Cobb", "Red Rory", "Young Wildcat" and "Marko the Miracle Man". These stories had no pictures apart from those on the title pages, but readers didn't mind. This was as near to real-life adventure as they could get!

YOUNG WILDCAT
LAST OF THE FIGHTING MAC...

...who won't score goals—until it is too late to win!

TRAINED TO BURST–UP
BALDY'S TEAM

Mike wins a cricket match—with a well-aimed kick!

THE FAMILY *MUST* BE CHAMPS!

DAD GRANDPA

MIKE WILLIE BOB JOE

Even bullets can't stop Buster from bringing in a new pupil!

A GUNMAN GUARDS THE ONE-MAN SCHOOL

Hawke fishes for a human shark—300 feet above the streets of Paris!

MARKO THE MIRACLE MAN

THIS IS A DIXON HAWKE STORY

Some events from 1947...
SAAB produced their first motor car.
Pakistan and India gained independence from Great Britain.
26 inches of snow fell in New York in 16 hours.
Thor Heyerdahl completed his famous crossing of the Pacific Ocean on the balsa-wood craft, "Kon Tiki".
Ronald Colman won Best Actor Oscar for "A Double Life".

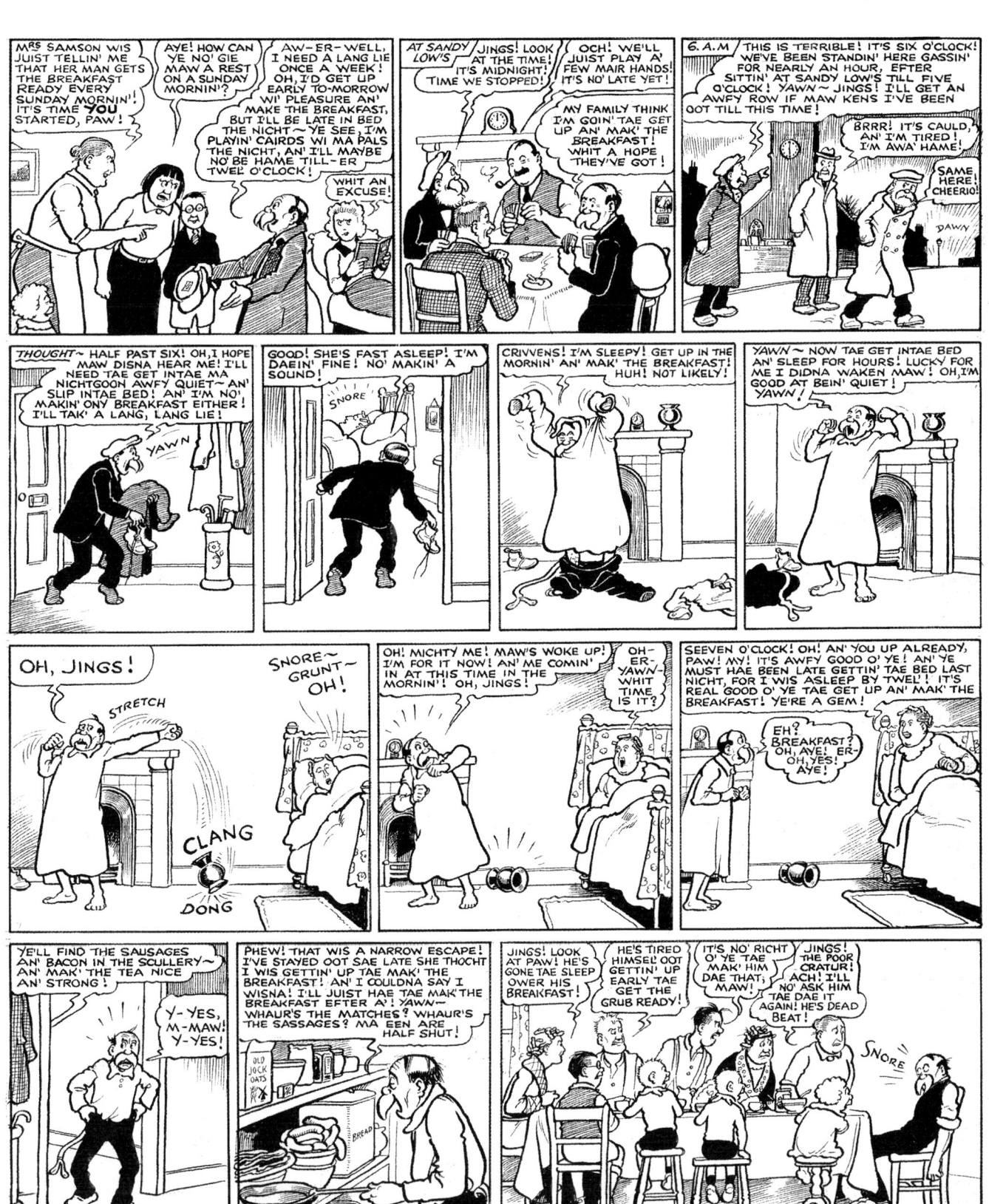

The Sunday Post 23rd February 1947

The Sunday Post 7th September 1947

The Sunday Post 13th April 1947

The Sunday Post 21st September 1947

The Sunday Post 24th August 1947

The Sunday Post 5th October 1947

The Sunday Post 7th September 1947

The Sunday Post 28th December 1947

1948

When Paw got back to Glebe Street after a hard day's work, he wouldn't be able to sit back and relax right away. The Twins would have to have a bath and Horace's homework might need to be checked. Even after that, there would still be a bedtime story to read to the Bairn and shoes to be polished ready for the morning. Then, at last, he could light his pipe, put his feet up, switch on the radio and catch up on some reading.

The SCOTS MAGAZINE

The SCOTS MAGAZINE
APRIL 1948
ONE SHILLING

The SCOTS MAGAZINE
MAY 1948
ONE SHILLING

Spring Comes To Ben Lomond

May Meeting — Scotland's Kirk Assembles

Newspapers were never far from Paw's side, but when it came to other reading, he would probably have opted for the "Scots Magazine". This packed publication contained all the stories folk like Paw loved — tales from the Highlands and Lowlands and features about Scotland's glorious history and famous places. One magazine could keep him going all month.

Some events from 1948...
Mahatma Gandhi, leader of India's National Congress, was murdered.
London hosted the Olympic Games.
World Health Organisation was formed by the United Nations.
The Arab-Israeli war began.
The British government introduced The National Health Service.

BRECHIN   Founded 990. Refounded 1150. Reconstructed 1806.

Books and Other Things
A REVIEW OF CURRENT SCOTS LETTERS
By THE EDITOR

Mr Poucher's Camera : The Gracious Garden :
Remember With a Doll : John Brown's Phantasy : A
Modern Pennant : The Fringe of the Hills : A Great
Chancellor : The Scottish Nation : Philosopher's Stone.

"My dearest love, she is to me
Refreshing stream, and shady tree.
Her kindliness, where'er I turn,
Runs near me like a Highland burn ;
And every pine and every fir
Are doubly dear because of her."

THE above verse was written long ago from pleasant
memories of the tree and the burn, a reproduction
from a photograph of which appears on the jacket of
Mr W. A. Poucher's "A Camera in the Cairngorms" (London :
Chapman and Hall, 21s net). And many more are the
memories brought back these winter nights as your eye
recreates from Mr Poucher's beautiful photographs the actual
places, where perchance you have enjoyed high adventure, or
pleasant peace. Mr Poucher takes you wander all Upper Deeside with him
Lochnagar. Then you walk through the Lairig—and a really
from Ballater to Braemar, and so on to the Linn. Now you
climb and climb until all MacDhui's wonders can be laid
before you ; now you walk through the Lairig—and a really
magnificent picture is the one entitled "Looking Back to the
Lairig Ghru from the first Pines of Rothiemurchus." The
paths on the west side of the hills are given special treatment,
at last, looking across Loch Morlich to Carn Elrig at
dawn, you bid the hills "good-night."
Mr Poucher gives any number of valuable details in his
notes with regard to maps, weather, accommodation, geology,
while he has admirable notes on his methods of photo-
graphy. The end-papers hold a good map of the region. A

... to flowers in a beautifully-illust

407

THE SCOTS MAGAZINE

management of the Rev. George Candlish, The Gateway
Theatre in Elm Row has had, in its short 'prentice period, a
most gratifying success.
Recently Mr Robert Kemp's "Let Wives Tak Tent," a
translation of Moliere's "L'Ecole des Femmes," has been
occupying the stage of that Theatre. In the March issue of
"The Prompter," the organ of the Citizens' Theatre Society,
William Power has an interesting story to tell concerning
another Moliere play, "Don Juan."
"I saw the fine performance of 'Let Wives Tak Tent'."
... "Mr Power. That night my pillow book was a volume
of ... Don Juan. An editorial note, signed N. David,
... Bibliotheque Nationale containing another Moliere
... of this tellingly concise stage version
... se). Clerics declared it irreligious and
... d 1890 . . . there was a
... "m" . . . "Odeon" . . . His
... revival

This had involved backing.
Many ... jerks, detrimental to the springs and the back axle.
people have tried unsuccessfully to diagnose the
trouble at Kessock Ferry. Probably the standard of the
vessels used has been responsible to a great extent. Without
any political inference it may be mentioned that this Ferry
operated a quite satisfactory service as a private concern.

Municipal By-Election.
The first municipal by-election to be held in Scotland under
the Local Government Act is to take place in the Muirtown
Ward of Inverness on February 8. During the war, when
municipal by-elections were not permitted, Inverness got the
co-option habit, and eventually there were far too many
co-opted members on the Town Council. Even now, when
under the new Act local authorities are permitted to fill
vacancies by means of a by-election, there were still a few
members who voted in favour of filling the vacancy in
Muirtown Ward by co-option. This, they argue,
save expense. But, when it is considered ...
election will cost only about £50, it is ...
is not much substance in that ar...
didate has been nominated ...
may be that no others ...
remains that the ...
representative ...
for them i...

ST. MACHAR
Founded 6th century
Refounded 1136,
1282, 1370.
Destroyed between
1559 — 1688.

Founded 1159. Destroyed 155...

...athedrals

The Sunday Post 15th February 1948

The Sunday Post 15th February 1948

The Sunday Post 18th July 1948

The Sunday Post 22nd February 1948

The Sunday Post 25th July 1948

The Sunday Post 11th July 1948

The Sunday Post 8th August 1948

The Sunday Post 8th August 1948

The Sunday Post 17th October 1948

The Sunday Post 5th September 1948

The Sunday Post 14th November 1948

The Sunday Post 26th December 1948

1949

Thanks to her good-looks, Maggie was seldom without a boyfriend. Almost every night she'd be washing her hair, putting on make-up and looking out her best clothes ("dolling herself up", as Paw put it!) to get ready for her latest date. And romantic reading material would always be the first choice of girls like Maggie.

The PAPER with the BEST STORIES On Sale Every Th.

No. 701   MAY 14, 1949   PRICE 2D.

SECRETS

THE HUSBAND YOU KILLED WILL HAUNT YOU IN THIS HOUSE!

THURSDAY

The PAPER with the BEST STORIES

No. 713   AUG. 6, 1949   PRICE 2D.

SECRETS

A SCENE FROM THE COMPLETE STORY INSIDE

THE Stranger SHE LOVED

One of the most popular story magazines of 1949 was "Secrets". Stories such as "Her Kind Of Man", "Wedding-eve Warning" and "The Wife Nobody Knew About" allowed young women to escape into a world where romance — and excitement — was never far away.

When Judy was in a fighting mood even the referee ran for shelter!

Plenty of PUNCH about JUDY

Some events from 1949...
The musical "South Pacific" opened on Broadway.
George Orwell's novel "1984" was published.
The People's Republic of China was formed.
Siam officially changed its name to Thailand.
The first non-stop around-the-world 'plane flight took place.

more she attracted him, the more determined he was to keep her at a distance!

Her Kind of Man

The Only Girl in FORGOTTEN VALLEY

the two girls as they really were—and which was the one for him.

The Sunday Post 30th January 1949

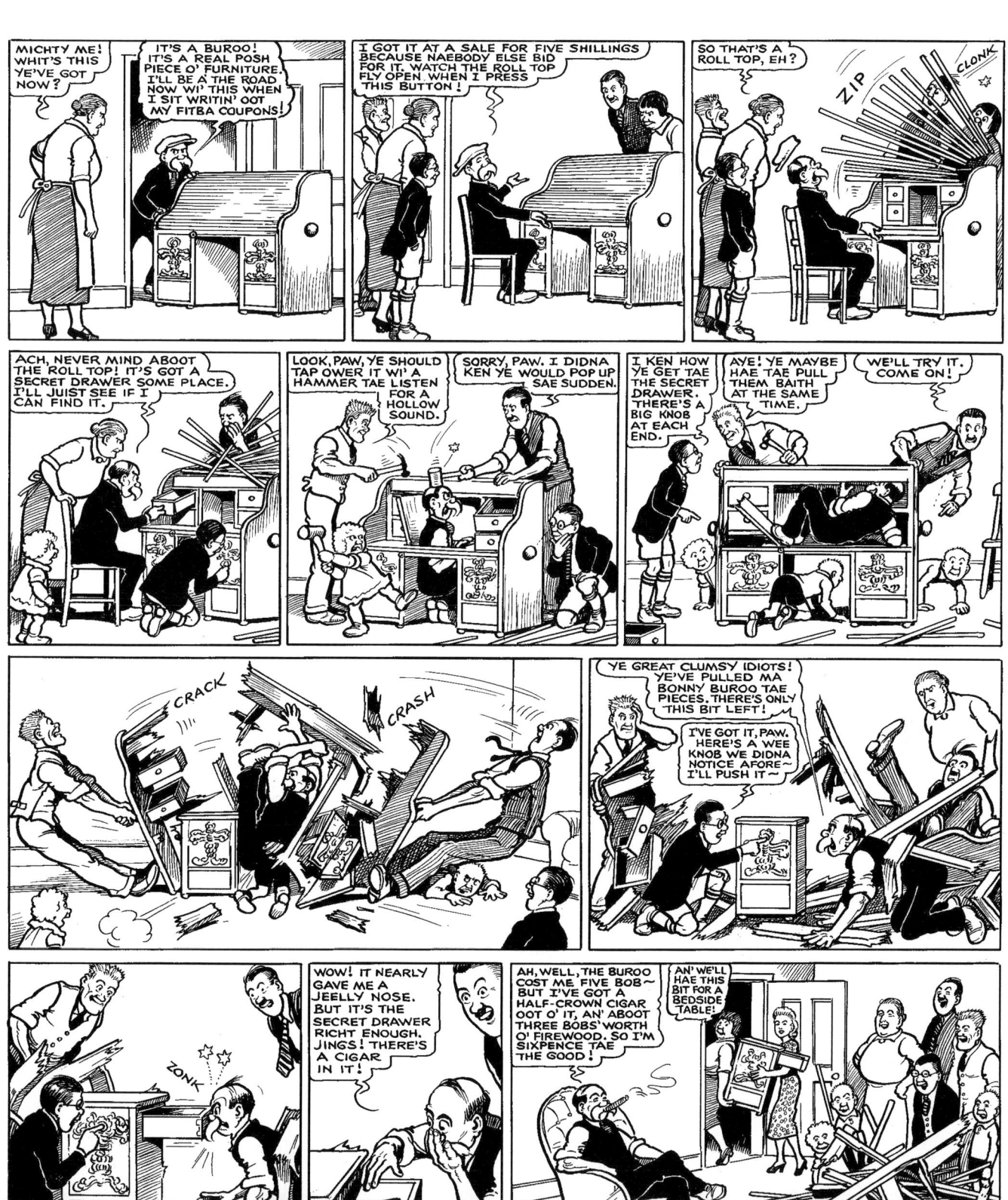

The Sunday Post 27th March 1949

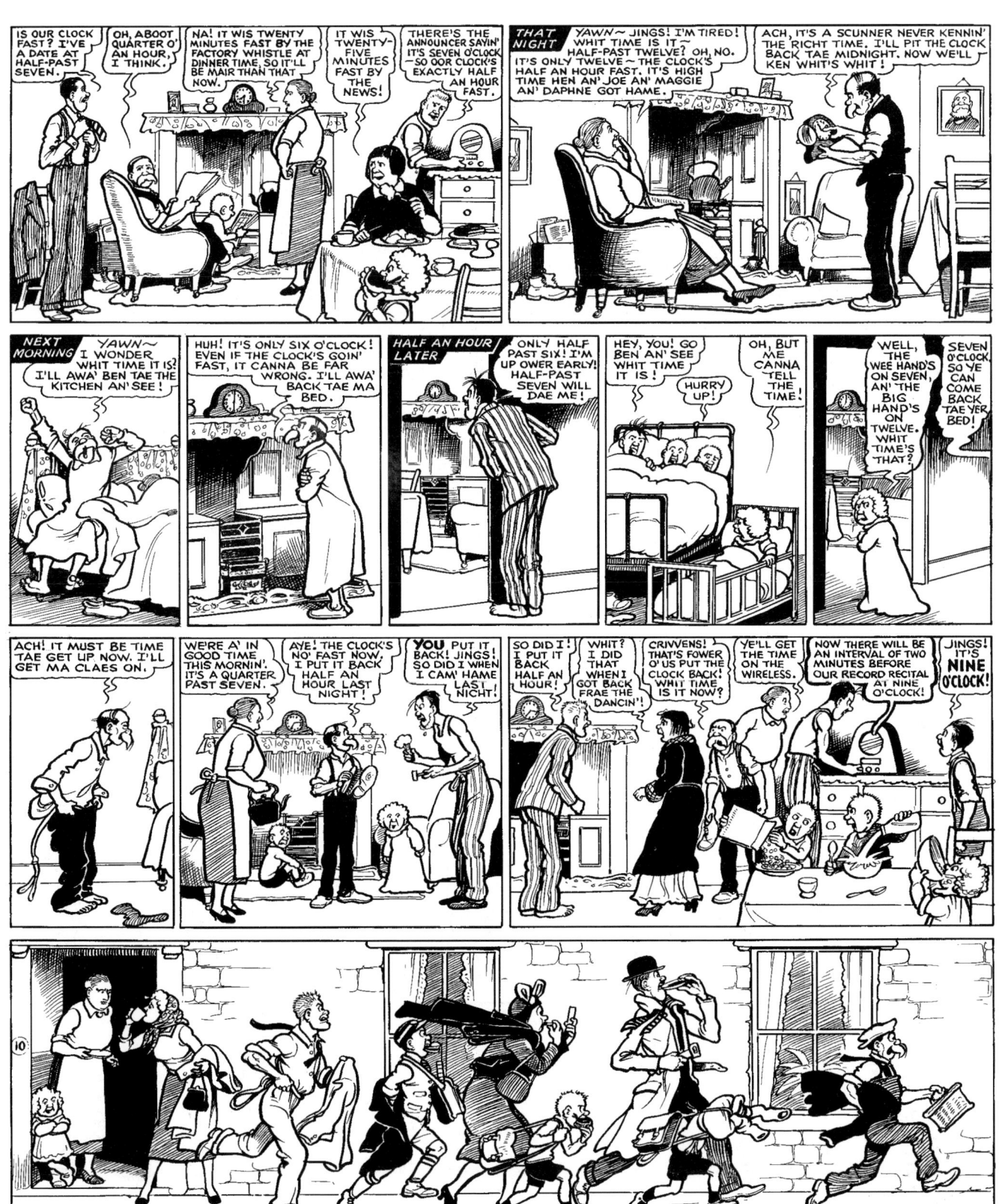

The Sunday Post 24th April 1949

The Sunday Post 29th May 1949

The Sunday Post 24th July 1949

The Sunday Post 2nd October 1949

The Sunday Post 7th August 1949

The Sunday Post 30th October 1949

The Sunday Post 14th August 1949

50

The Sunday Post 20th November 1949

1950

The Twins were the exact opposite of their brother Horace, who would spend many hours reading his schoolbooks. Like many other lads of their age, the Twins much preferred comics and, although their choice of comic might change from week to week, "The Beano" was always popular. "Biffo the Bear" was a particular favourite with everyone, but boys might argue over the merits of "Deep Sea Danny's Iron Fish" and "Tom Thumb's Schooldays". However, with funny picture stories such as "Pansy Potter", "Ding Dong Belle" and "Lord Snooty" also included in the comic, there was more than enough to take the Twins' minds off homework!

Some events from 1950...
The Korean War began.
Uruguay beat Brazil 2-1 in the football World Cup Final.
The comic strip "Peanuts" was first published.
Mother Teresa began her charity work in Calcutta.
Annapurna, the tenth-highest mountain in the world, was climbed for the first time.

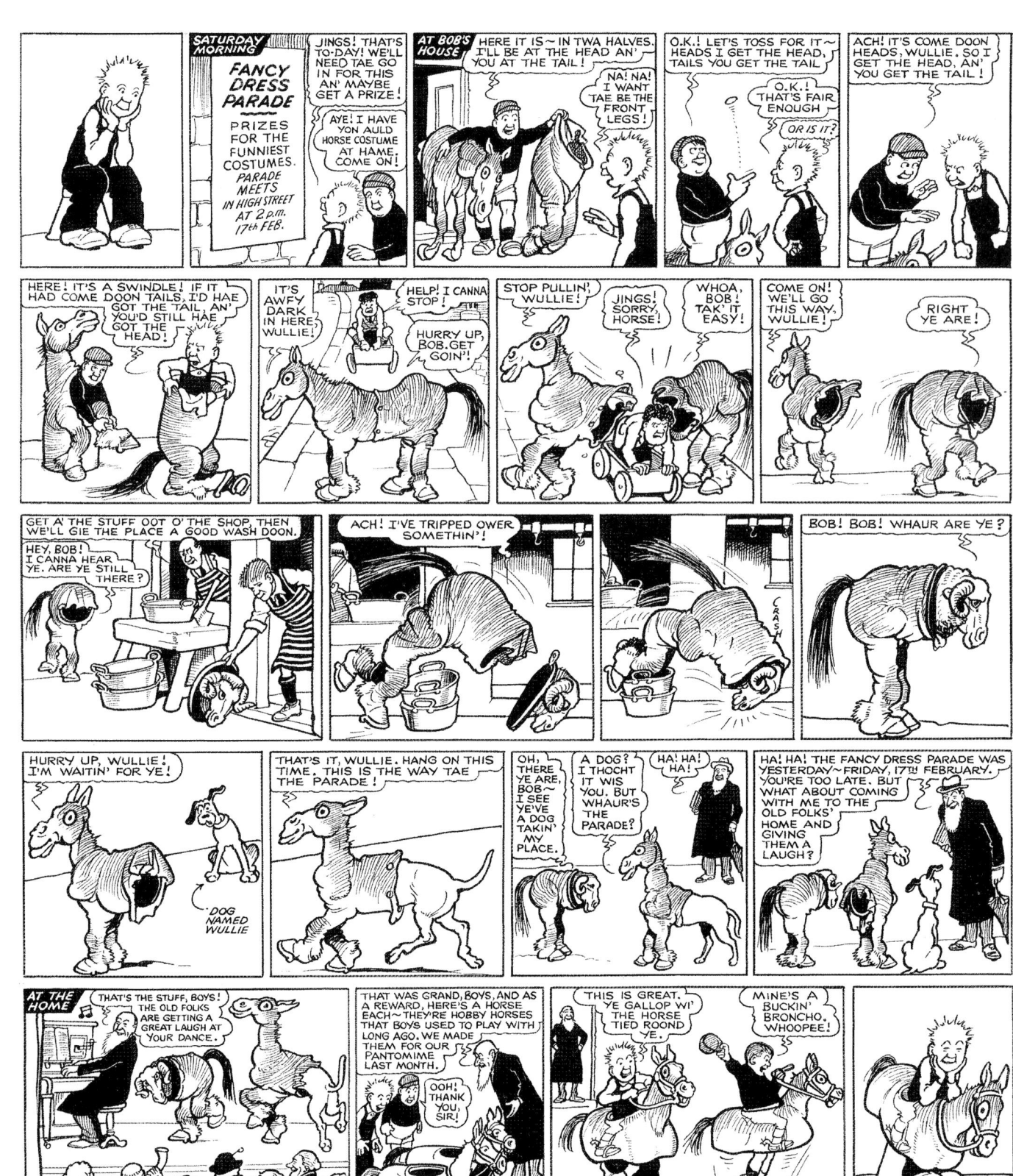

The Sunday Post 2nd July 1950

The Sunday Post 18th June 1950

The Sunday Post 20th August 1950

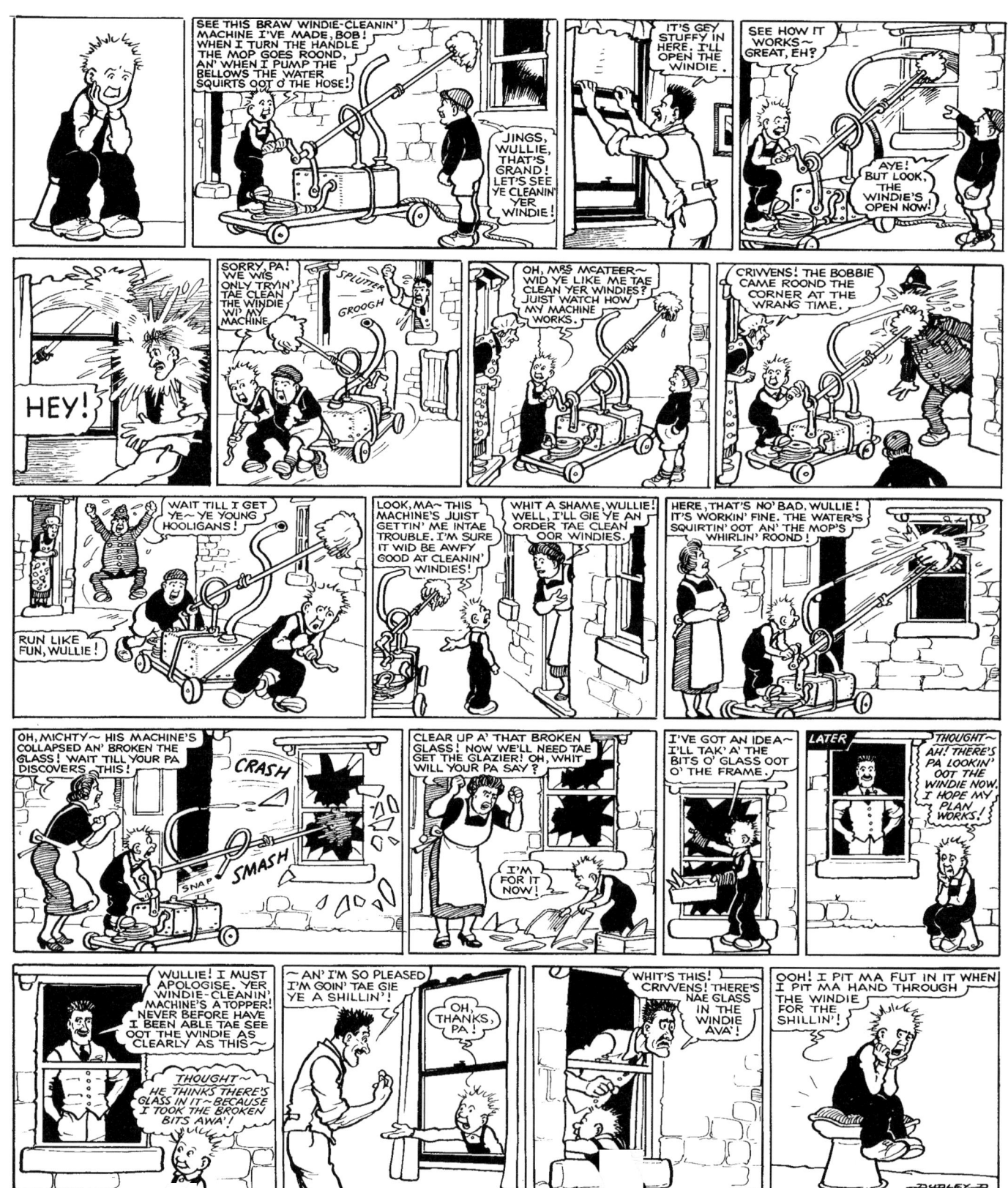

The Sunday Post 16th July 1950

The Sunday Post 24th September 1950

OOR WULLIE 1946-1956 THE GOLDEN YEARS

The Sunday Post 8th October 1950

The Sunday Post 5th November 1950

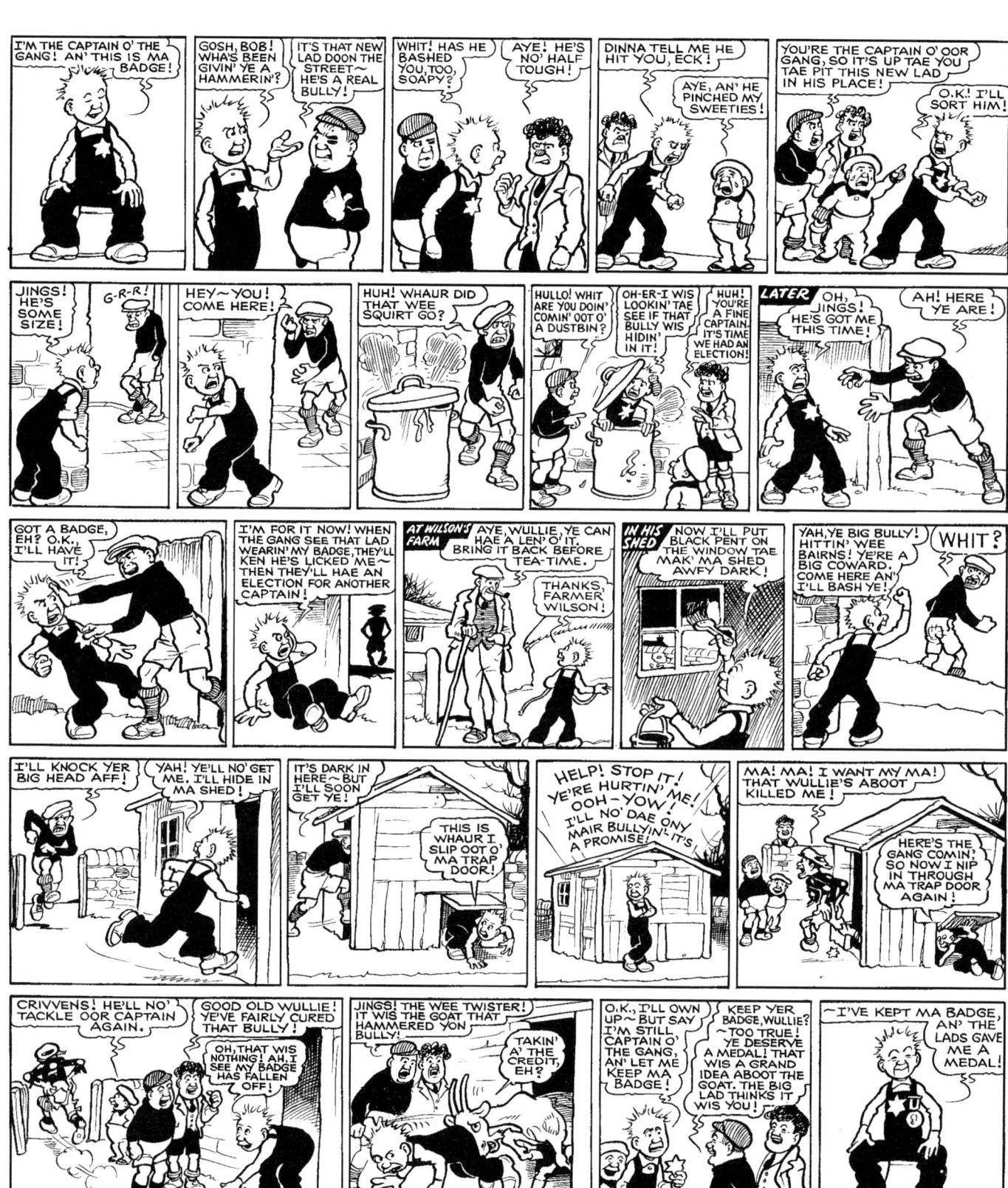

The Sunday Post 12th November 1950

When Gran'paw moved in for six weeks at the end of 1950, things were far from harmonious — as this instalment shows.

Of course, all ended happily, with Gran'paw moving back to his ain wee house, and things returning to 'normal' in Glebe Street.

The Sunday Post 3rd December 1950

1951

Maw Broon always appeared to run the home like a well-oiled machine. If something needed doing, she'd do it – whether it be helping Horace with his homework, finishing a dress pattern for Daphne or completing a jig-saw that Joe had been stuck on for weeks. But at night, when the Twins and Bairn were in their beds, Maw, like thousands of other mothers up and down the country, turned to her favourite magazine – "The People's Friend".

GREAT NEW STORY "HOLD IN YOUR KEEPING

People's Fri

No. 4267.

NOVEMBER 3, 1951.

J. Campbell Kerr.

SPECIAL THIS WEEK ● Model Patterns for a Party Dress

People's Friend

Price 3D.

DECEMBER 8, 1951.

No. 4272.

The "Friend" was loved by many and one copy was often handed round whole streets or closes. Maw could enjoy the romantic stories like "A Stranger To Them All", "If Today Be Sweet" and "Young MacAlpin's Choice", before copying down the recipes and doing the puzzles – if somebody hadn't filled them in before the magazine reached her, that is!

Some events from 1951…
"An American in Paris", starring Gene Kelly, won the Oscar for best picture.
Argentinian Juan Fangio won the Formula One Championship.
A nuclear bomb was tested by the United States.
An avalanche in the Alps killed 240 and left 45,000 temporarily buried.
The world's first commercial computer, the "UNIVAC", was delivered to the United States Census Bureau.

The Sunday Post 14th January 1951

The Sunday Post 11th February 1951

68

The Sunday Post 25th March 1951

The Sunday Post 4th March 1951

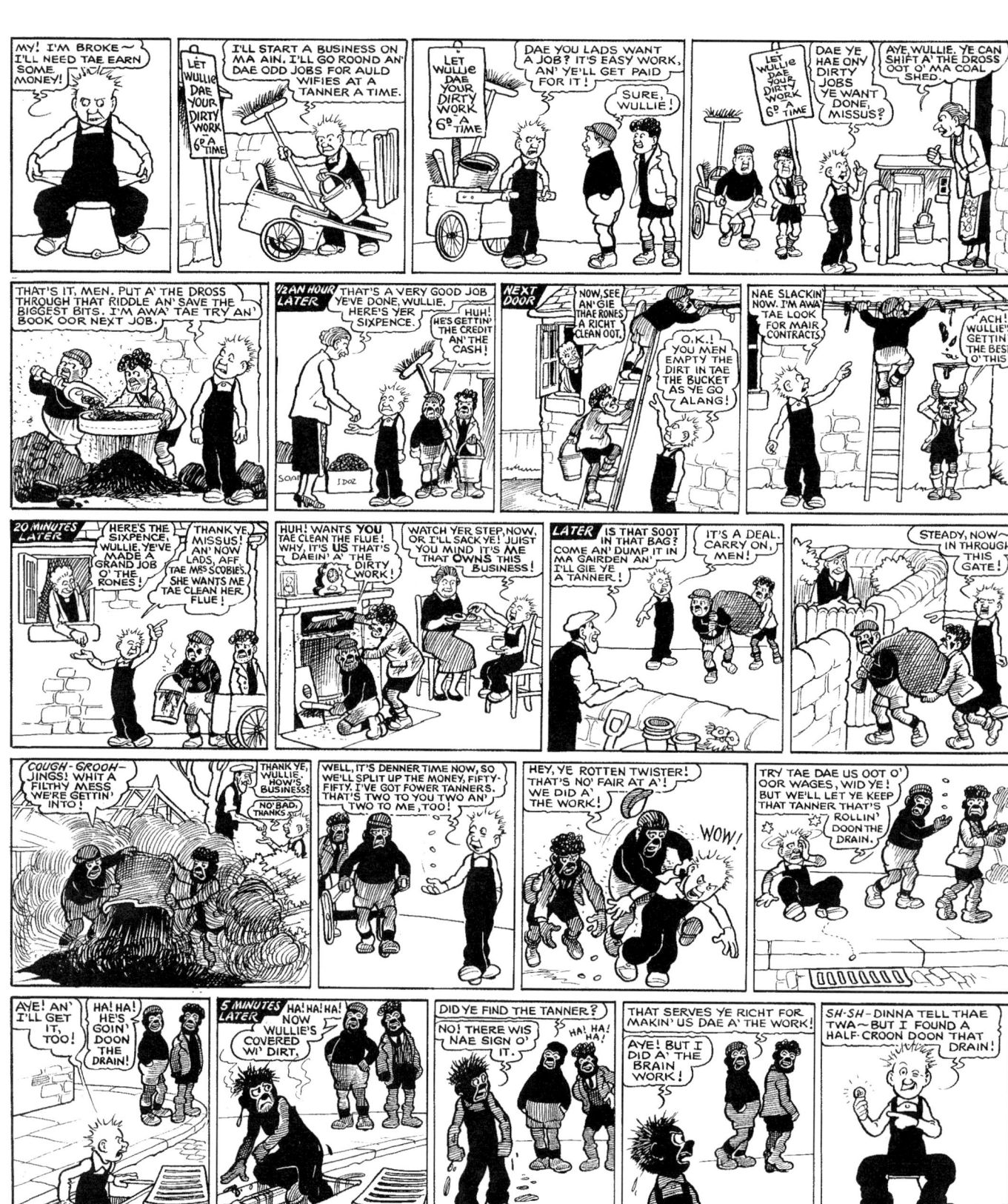

The Sunday Post 27th May 1951

The Sunday Post 25th March 1951

The Sunday Post 3rd June 1951

The Sunday Post 13th May 1951

The Sunday Post December 9th 1951

The Sunday Post 12th August 1951

The Sunday Post December 16th 1951

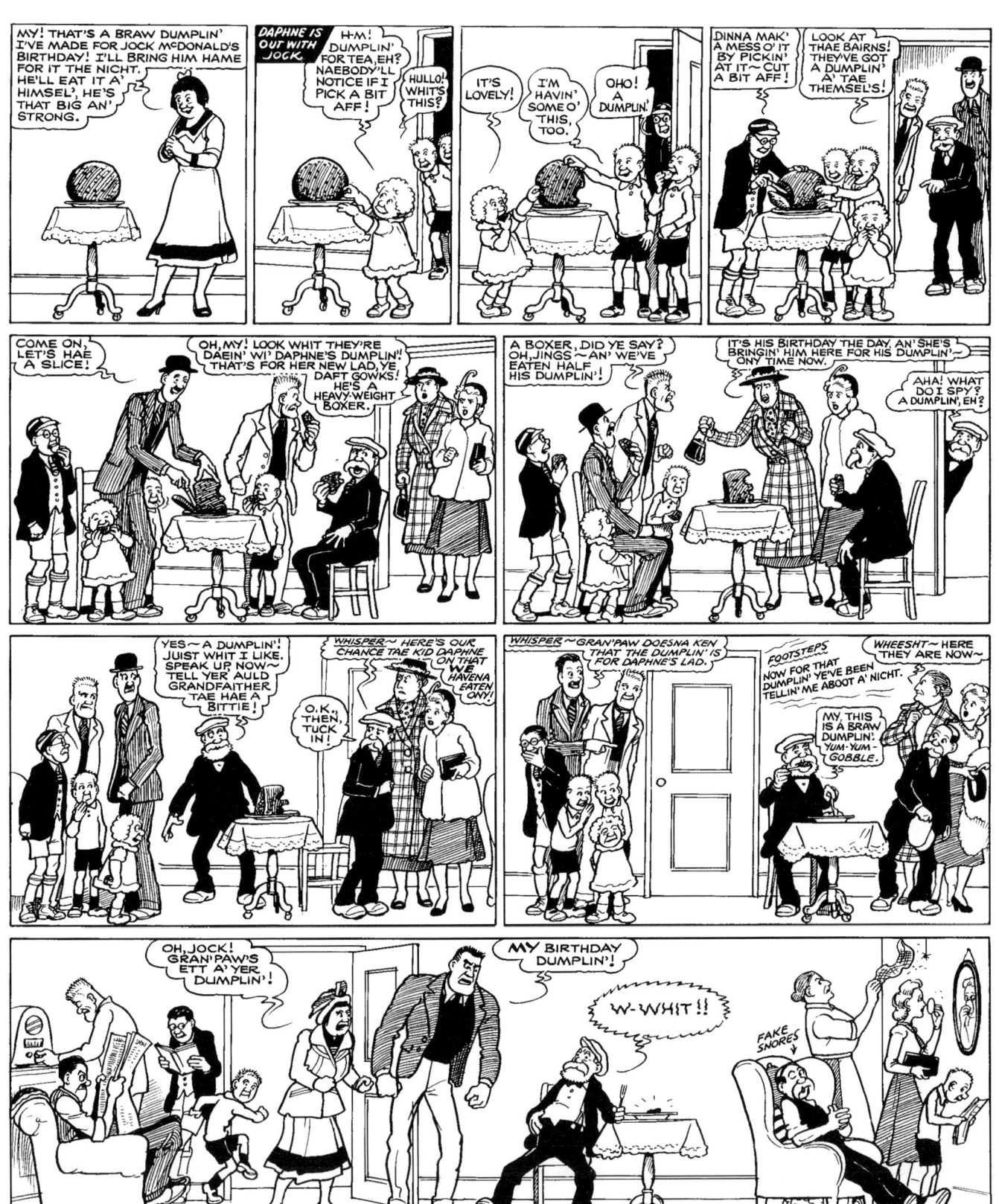

The Sunday Post 21st October 1951

1952

Joe, the sportsman of the family, was passionate about football — both watching or playing. Every Sunday morning — sometimes before the others were awake — he would walk down to the newsagents to pick up "The Sunday Post" to check on the football reports. The others knew they wouldn't get a look in until every inch of the sports pages had been read.

THE SUNDAY POST, JANUARY 6, 1952

The Sunday Post

NO. 2419 [REGISTERED AT THE GENERAL POST OFFICE AS A NEWSPAPER] PRINTED AND PUBLISHED EVERY SUNDAY MORNING SUNDAY, JANUARY 6, 1952 Radio—Pa

Cock-a-Hoop Carlsen Ho

Reach Port Wednesday

3-KNOT TOW TO SAFETY

SKIPPER Kurt Carlsen, still aboard hi crippled, heavily-listing ship, radioed last night th enterprise e a million dollars." the Flying Enterprise was ed three knots by the 'port by noon, W osition

(caption) reviews a United States Army Guard of Honour on his arrival Army Base Pier, New York yesterday. Between Mr Churchill and the he left is New York's official "greeter", Grover Whalen. (Picture wired last night from New York via London to Glasgow.)

N injur heavi landin, Icelan Dakota U.S.A.F Lancashi

Three Statio engine to the orderlies rushin were thrown pulled to safety other burns, injuries, an into the crum

"Our C Bombed Chines

CHINA'S truce negotiat American planes had yes Chinese cities of Shanghai, Ha Tsingtan. The same accusation previously made by the Peiv Acrimony without progress up yesterday's talks. You've far bringing peace and hope an said General Hsien.

The Sunday Post

Morning Special

THE SUNDAY POST, SEPTEMBER 21, 1952

PRINTED AND PUBLISHED EVERY SUNDAY MORNING Radio, TV—Page 4 PRICE 2½d

SUNDAY, SEPTEMBER 21, 1952

NO. 2456 [REGISTERED AT THE GENERAL POST OFFICE AS A NEWSPAPER]

FIRST TO WELCOME THE ARGYLLS

WHEN the Empire Halladale arrives at the Tail o' the Bank, Greenock, tomorrow afternoon the Argyll and Sutherland Highlanders will be given their first official welcome home.

The provosts of Greenock, Gourock, Dunoon, and Port-Glasgow will go out from Princes Pier, Gourock, in a tender to board the Empire Halladale and talk with some of the officers and men.

Also in the tender will be a party of the 8th Battalion Argylls, accompanied by a piper. As the tender goes alongside the piper will play the regiment's march. ("The Campbells Are Coming".)

(See also Page 8.)

R.A.F. PROBES FLYING SAUCER REPORT

ALL DETAILS BEING SENT TO EXPERTS IN FIFE

REPORTS that a "flying saucer" had been sighted by airmen taking part in the 8-nations naval exercise, "Mainbrace," are being treated seriously by the R.A.F.

It was emphasised at Pitreavie, Fife, Maritime H.Q. yesterday.

But the experts are not expressing an opinion until there has been a chance of studying fuller reports.

No. 18 Group Coastal Command, whose men sighted the mysterious object, has asked for more details. Examination of these further details will take several days more.

It was emphasised that the object had been seen by ten officers and men who told the same story.

They stated they had seen a white, circular objec in the sky five miles behind a Meteor jet-plane, flyin near the North Riding R.A.F. station at Topcliffe.

The station intelligence officer signalled to H.Q. an was seen at 15,000 feet, was silver in colour, and wa moving at a comparatively slow speed on a cours similar to the Meteor.

Before it began to descend it maintained a slow forward speed, and then began to drop, swinging in a pendulum motion like a falling autumn leaf.

The observers thought it might be a parachute or cooling from the Meteor, but the R.A.F. stated yester day that none had been found in the vicinity.

"Incredible Speed"

When the aircraft turned towards the R.A.F. station at Dishforth, the object, still descending, seemed to follow.

The pendulum motion and the descent stopped. Th began to rotate about its own axis.

accelerated, "at incredible speed," in a south-east course, an seconds.

U.S. Backs Jap Cotton Plan

BRITISH HOPES FADE

BRITISH hopes for some kind of agreement under which the Japanese would restrain their ambitions in the world cotton market seemed last night to be almost certainly doomed to disappointment.

This was clear from the preliminary skirmishing between the international delegations at the cotton conference at Buxton, Derbyshire. The nations represented account for 90% of the world's cotton goods output.

Already the attitude of the American and Japanese delegates is clear. The Japanese are all out for unrestricted assault on the world markets and the Americans see no reason why not.

In this week's talks the American delegation is certain to come out against any plan which would provide a system of guaranteed markets for British and Japanese producers.

U.S. WELCOME FOR CHURCHILL

"PROSPECTS ARE SOLID"

the Western world—Mr Churchill met in Washington yesterday, and these y Britain's Prime Minister to America's watching world:

together, each doing loyally his best view and the differences of interests all find ourselves safe at the end of gth bring peace and hope and nkind."

When Mr Churchill stepped from e President's plane after the flight m New York. Mr Truman met with a warm handclasp and a smile.

ut Britain and the Common and the U.S. are the closest lds, and we want them to way," he said.

oastguard cutter took Mr to Brooklyn, New York, ween Mary as soon as she ' York's quarantine

"g Conclusions"

settled so much se and intimate in the heads of both sides of an deal with knowledge view were

a lot of clusions friendly a their little

ADMIRAL AND FAMILY KILLED

REAR-ADMIRAL T. H. Simpson his wife, son, and daughter were killed last night when their ca crashed head-on with a motor coacl on the St Albans road at St Albans, Herts.

FOUR HURT IN CITY CRASH

Four people, including a boy of six, were injured when the van they were travelling in collided with a drive and Balmore Road, Glasgow, last night.

The injured were—Evan Dunn (6), his father, William Dun and his mother, Jame Dun of Hartsmore Dun

---

And even after that, men like Joe would find lots to interest them. The news both local and international was up-to-date, and there was always the light relief of "Merry Mac's Fun Parade". But if they weren't careful, the women in the family would sneak the paper from under their noses and have a quick look at "Pricilla's Page", one of the Post's most popular columns for young ladies!

(caption) Making his first personal appearance, 10-week-old Peter Grant Palethorpe Todd after hi christening at Stubbings Church, near Maidenhead. Proud papa, film star Richard Todd, might have told Peter that cameras are not like when you get used to them. Keeping motherly eye on things is Mrs Todd, former Glasgow repertory actress Catherine Grant Bogle.

ICE-CAP RESCUE BID TODAY

IF weather permits, it is hoped an American Dakota aircraft fitted with skis will today attempt to rescue the 12 airmen from an R.A.F. Hastings plane marooned on a Greenland ice-cap since Tuesday. This was stated on Tuesday night by the Air Ministry, who received the news in a signal from Squadron-Leader Eric Robinson, leader of 500 miles from the spot where Robinson re-

MACLEAN AND BURGESS REPORTED IN BERLIN

ALLIES DENY EAST GERMAN STATESMAN'S STORY

THE missing British diplomats, Guy Burgess and Donald MacLean, are in Berlin, according to the East German Premier, Nuschke.

Herr Nuschke's statement was made at a lunch given by the Foreign Association in Bonn.

(caption) MACLEAN. BURGESS.

FIRE THREAT TO 5000 CASKS OF WHISKY

could unusual current the sun shining on the have seen it the appearance flying saucer."

ATTACKED AFTEF OLD FIRM DERBY

WALKING along London Road Glasgow, after the Celtic Rangers match at Parkhead yeste day. Frank Duffy, and Charles McLea Street Paisley, and of Motherwell Road, Carfi number of men

Some events from 1952...
Elizabeth II became Queen on the death of her father George VI.
The "Diary of Anne Frank" was published.
The film "The African Queen" opened in New York.
"The Flower Pot Men" premiered on BBC television.
Finland hosted the Summer Olympics.

The Sunday Post 1st June 1952

The Sunday Post 27th January 1952

The Sunday Post 6th July 1952

The Sunday Post 23rd March 1952

The Sunday Post 20th July 1952

The Sunday Post 1st June 1952

The Sunday Post 17th August 1952

The Sunday Post 29th June 1952

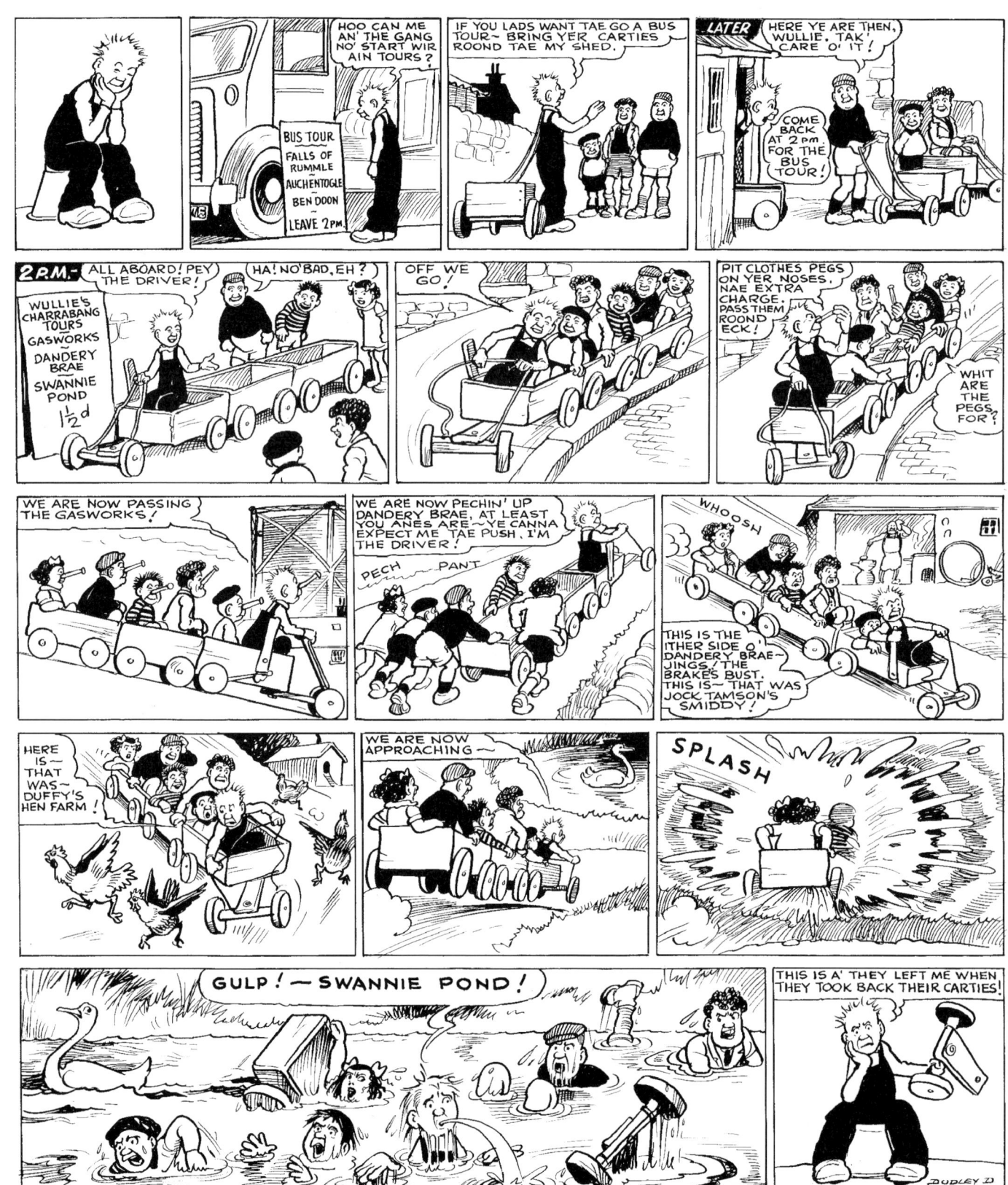

The Sunday Post 24th August 1952

The Sunday Post 5th October 1952

The Sunday Post 31st August 1952

The Sunday Post 23rd November 1952

1953

Granpaw Broon always seemed to have lots to keep him occupied — a game of bools with his pals or simply sitting on the park bench watching the world go by. However, he also liked to spend as much time as he could with the rest of the family at Number 10, playing games with the youngsters, finishing off Paw's crosswords — or sneaking a sly look at one of the comics left lying around.

DON'T MISS THE BIG MYSTERY YARN—"THE

THE ROVER

No. 1453—MAY 2nd, 1953. EVE

THERE'S A FREE GIFT—"THE MAGIC EYE"—INSIDE THIS PAPER!

THE ROVER

No. 1473—SEPT. 19th, 1953. EVERY THURSDAY. PRICE 3d.

ANOTHER BIG SURPRISE!
TWO 36-PAGE BOOKLETS FREE TO EVERY READER NEXT WEEK!
MORE ABOUT THESE FREE GIFTS INSIDE.

A CHANCE for you TO GET YOUR SCHOOL BADGE IN "THE ROVER" NOW!

School Badges
WORN BY READERS
YOU CAN GET YOUR SCHOOL BADGE IN "THE ROVER." SEND IT IN NOW.

Granpaw, like many grown men, was a big bairn when it came to comics, and "The Rover" was a great favourite with laddies of all ages. Often men would pick it up because they saw the badge of their old school on the front cover and, from then on, they would become avid readers of stories like "It's Goals That Count", "Morgyn The Mighty" and "I Flew With Braddock". Escapism at its best.

Some events from 1953...
Russian dictator Joseph Stalin died on March 5th.
Golfer Ben Hogan won the US Masters, US Open and Open Championships.
In July, the Korean War ended.
The current affairs programme "Panorama" was launched on BBC television.
The "Topper" was first published.

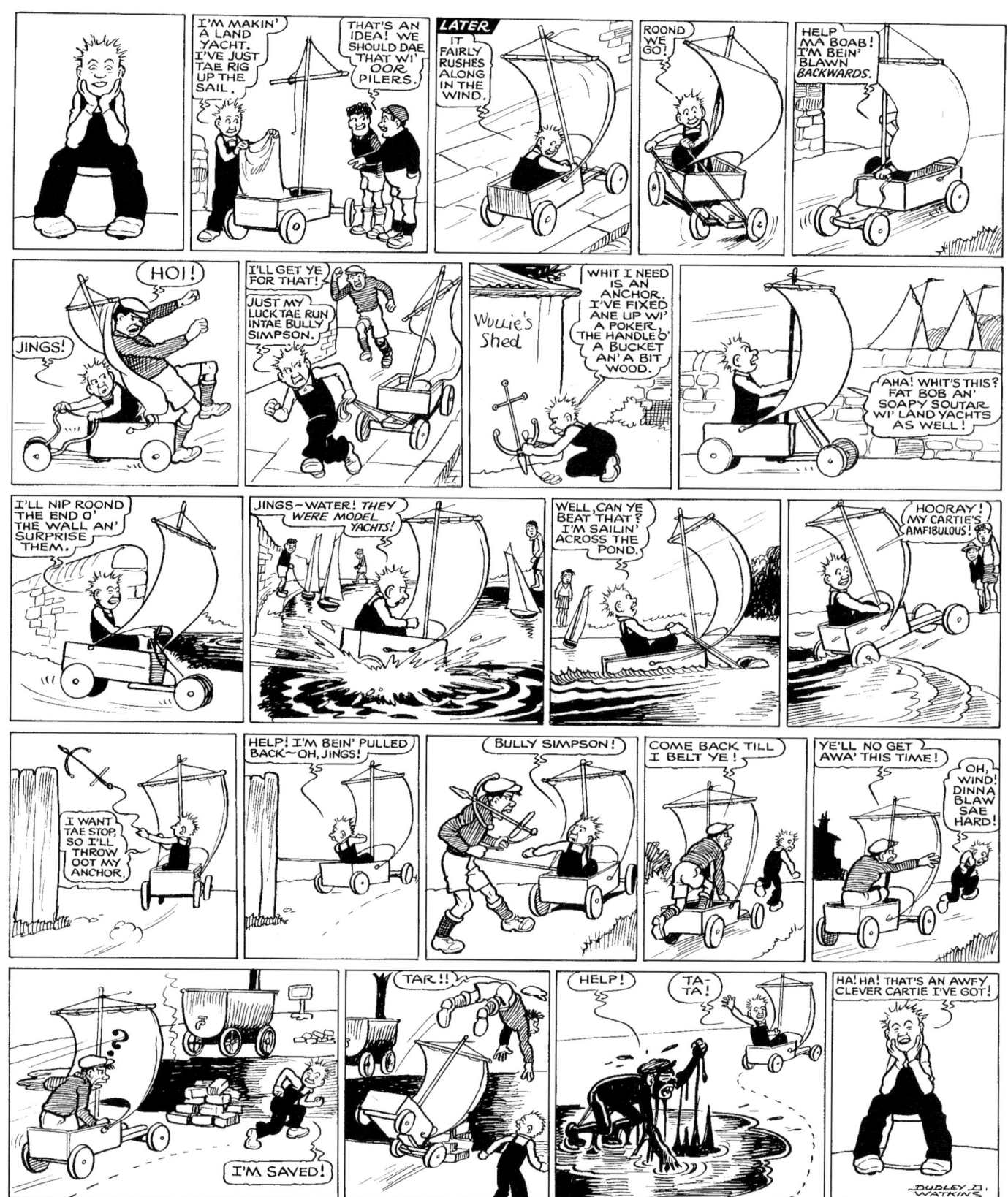

The Sunday Post 11th January 1953

The Sunday Post 15th March 1953

The Sunday Post 19th July 1953

The Sunday Post 26th April 1953

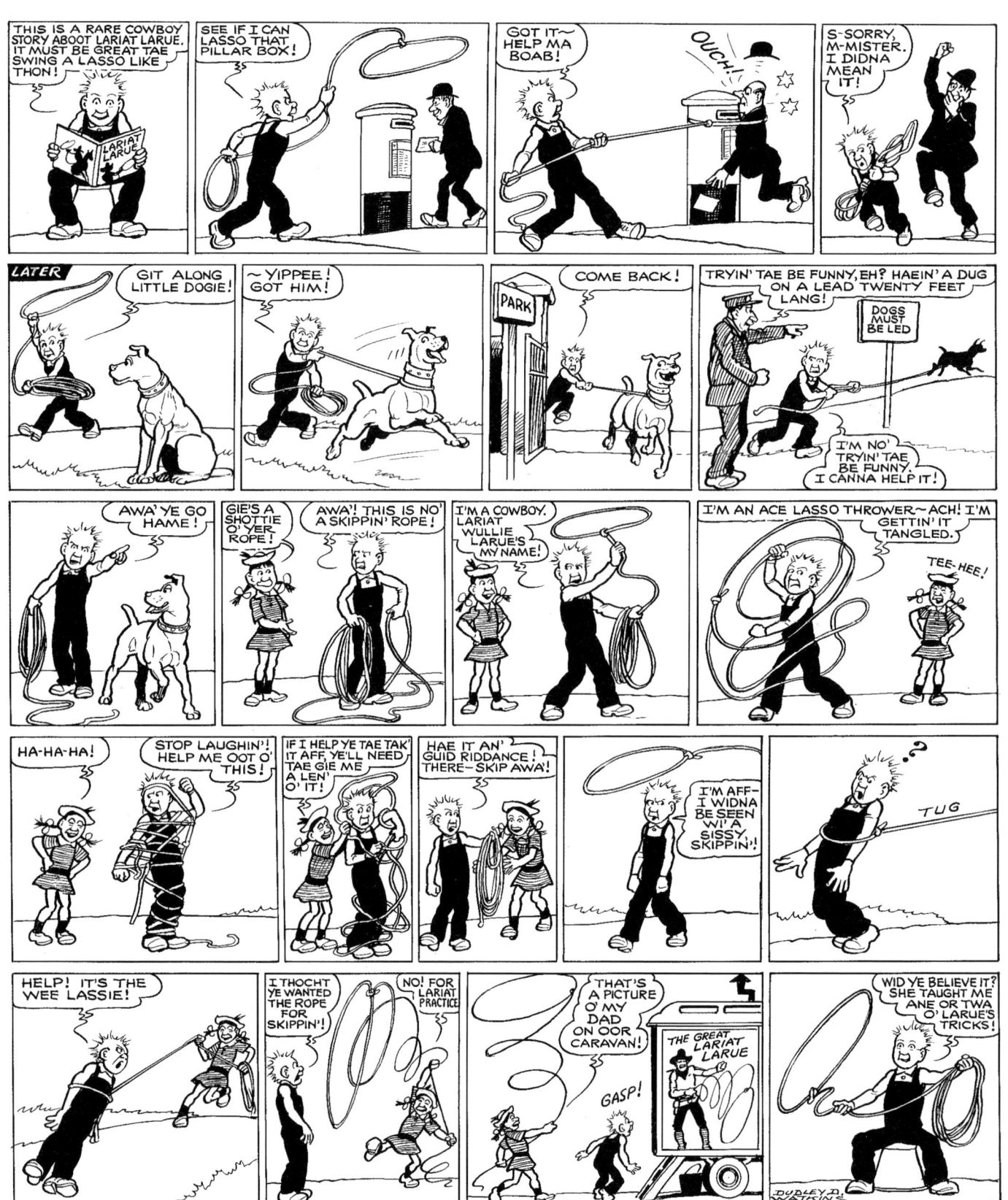

The Sunday Post 13th September 1953

The Sunday Post 14th June 1953

The Sunday Post 18th October 1953

The Sunday Post 12th July 1953

The Sunday Post 15th November 1953

The Sunday Post 1st November 1953

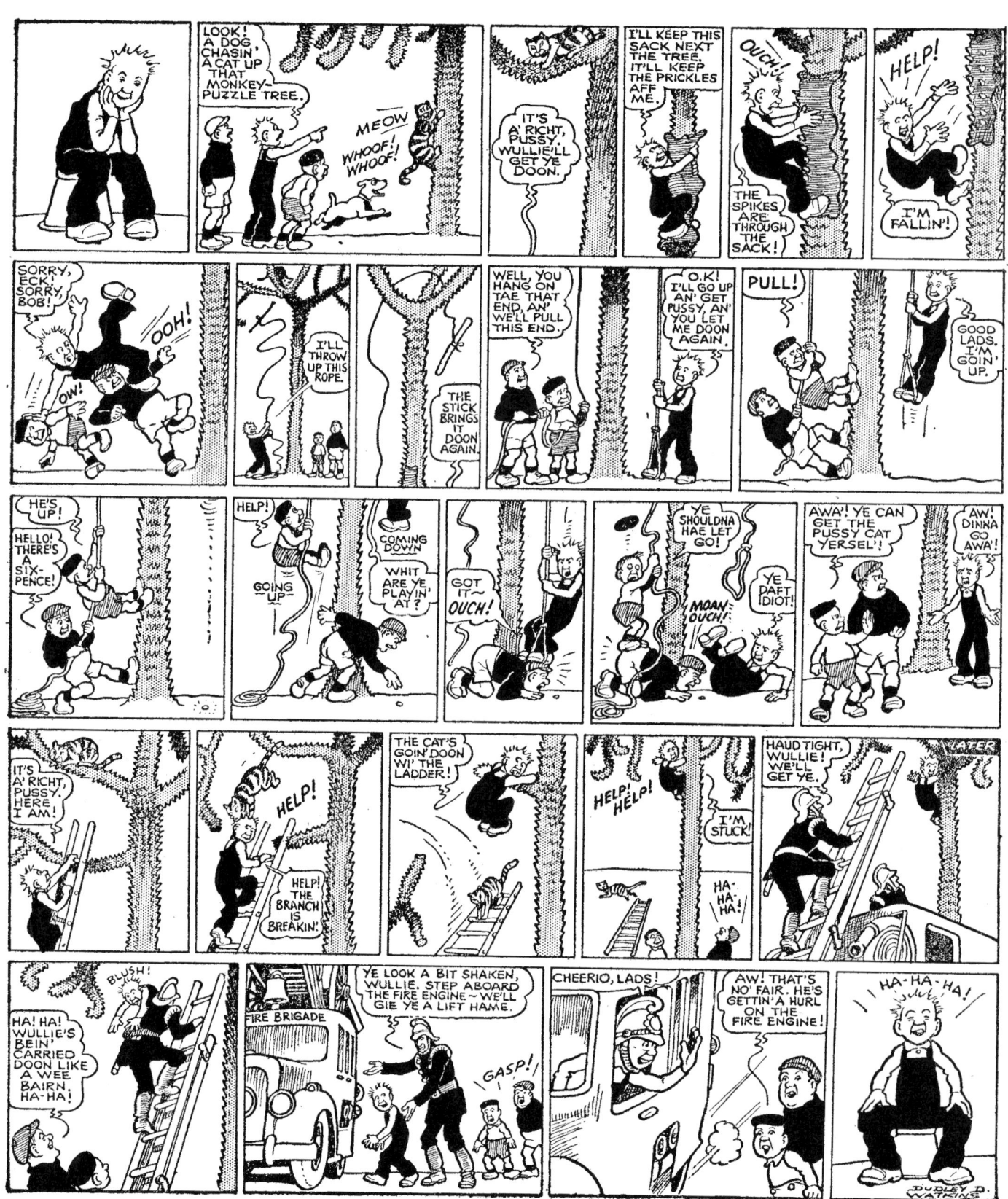

The Sunday Post 22nd November 1953

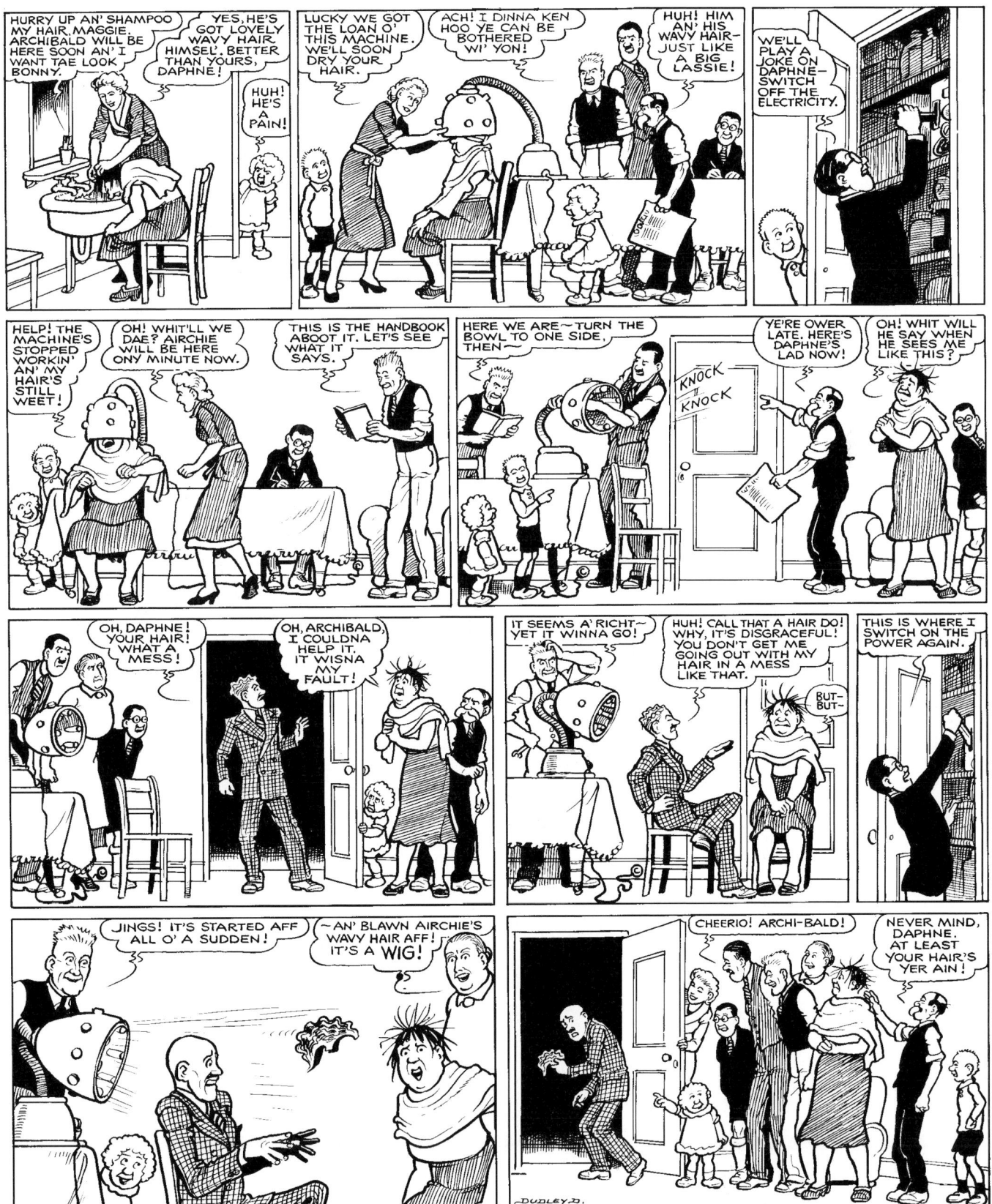

The Sunday Post 8th November 1953

1954

While the rest of the family could settle down to read their favourite comic, newspaper or magazine, tiny tots like the Bairn often felt a bit left out. They could enjoy looking at the colourful pictures in the comics, but they really needed someone to read the stories to them. However, with comics like "The Dandy" around, there were always plenty volunteers.

"Desperate Dan", with his funny bristly chin and super-powerful strength, was a favourite with "Bairns" everywhere — as were other funny pals like "Keyhole Kate", "Young Drake", "Great Big Bonzo" and "Hungry Horace". These adventures were fast-paced and easily read — making them ideal first reading for many.

Some events from 1954...
Food rationing ended in Britain.
UEFA (Union of European Football Associations) was formed in Basel, Switzerland.
Gamal Nasser was elected President of Egypt.
The first nuclear-powered submarine, USS Nautilus, was launched.
The last of 2,956 radio episodes of "The Lone Ranger" was broadcast.

I THINK WE'LL HAE A GAME O' CHICKY-MELLY TONIGHT.

WE FIX THE TACK TO THIS WINDOW FRAME. THE BUTTON HANGS AGAINST THE GLASS.

THEN WE PULL THIS END O' THE STRING AN' IT RATTLES. IT NEARLY DRIVES THEM DAFT!

YE WEE MONKEYS! YOU AN' YOUR CHICKY-MELLY!

HO-HO! WHIT'S GOIN' ON, EH?

HELP! IT'S P.C. MURDOCH!

NAMES, PLEASE! WE CANNA HAE THIS KIND O' THING GOIN' ON!

MY NAME'S WULLIE!

FAT BOB!

SOAPY SOUTAR!

A'RIGHT! YE'LL HEAR MORE ABOOT THIS ~ FINED, OR PRISON, MAYBE.

THIS IS TERRIBLE. I FEEL LIKE A CONVICK.

FANCY WEARIN' A SUIT WI' ARROWS ~ LIKE A MELON!

MELON? YE MEAN A FELON!

NEXT DAY. LOOK! THERE'S A PHOTIE O' P.C. MURDOCH WHEN HE WIS PLAYIN' FOR THE THISTLE IN NINETEEN OATCAKE!

MURDOCH

HE STILL FANCIES HIMSEL' AS A FITBA' PLAYER. WAIT ~ I'VE AN IDEA!

DAE YE HAVE A BIT BROKEN GLASS YE DINNA WANT?

GLAZIER

AYE. YE CAN HAVE THIS. ARE YE BUILDIN' A GREEN-HOOSE?

LATER. HERE'S P.C. MURDOCH NOW. DO YER STUFF, BOB!

WE SAW YER PHOTIE WHEN YE PLAYED FOR THE THISTLE, BUT I BET YE COULDNA KICK A BA' FOR NUTS NOW.

WHIT'S THAT? I'M AS GOOD AS EVER I WIS ~ WATCH THIS!

HELP! IT'S CURVIN' OVER THE WA'!

ON THE OTHER SIDE. THE STRING PULLED IT OWER. NOW I DROP THE BRICK!

SMASH! TINKLE! CRASH!

RUN, BOYS! WE'VE SMASHED A WINDOW!

WE'RE IN FOR IT NOW!

WELL, NAEBODY CAN SAY I DID IT!

IT WIS P.C. MURDOCH!

A-HEM- AH- ER- WHIT AM I RUNNIN' FOR?

YOU'LL FIND OOT IF THE WIFIE TELLS THE SERGEANT!

IF THE INSPECTOR ASKS US WHO DID IT, WE'RE SO HONEST, WE'LL JUST HAVE TO TELL!

SAY NOTHIN' ABOOT THIS, AN' I'LL FORGET ABOOT YOU ONES PLAYIN' CHICKY-MELLY. I DIDNA REALLY TAK' YER NAMES. I WIS ONLY KIDDIN'!

OH! THAT'S FINE. WE'RE ONLY KIDDIN', TOO. COME AN' LOOK!

YE SEE, THE BA' WIS TIED TO THE INSIDE O' THE WALL BY A STRING. SO WHEN YOU KICKED IT, IT CAME OVER ~ AN' THEN BOB DROPPED A BRICK ON TO A SHEET O' GLASS!

YE WEE MONKEYS ~ YE! BUT ANY MORE CHICKY-MELLY AN' IT WILL BE THE NICK!

OCH, AYE! P.C. MURDOCH'S A GREAT LAD.

DUDLEY D. WATKINS

The Sunday Post 7th February 1954

The Sunday Post 4th April 1954

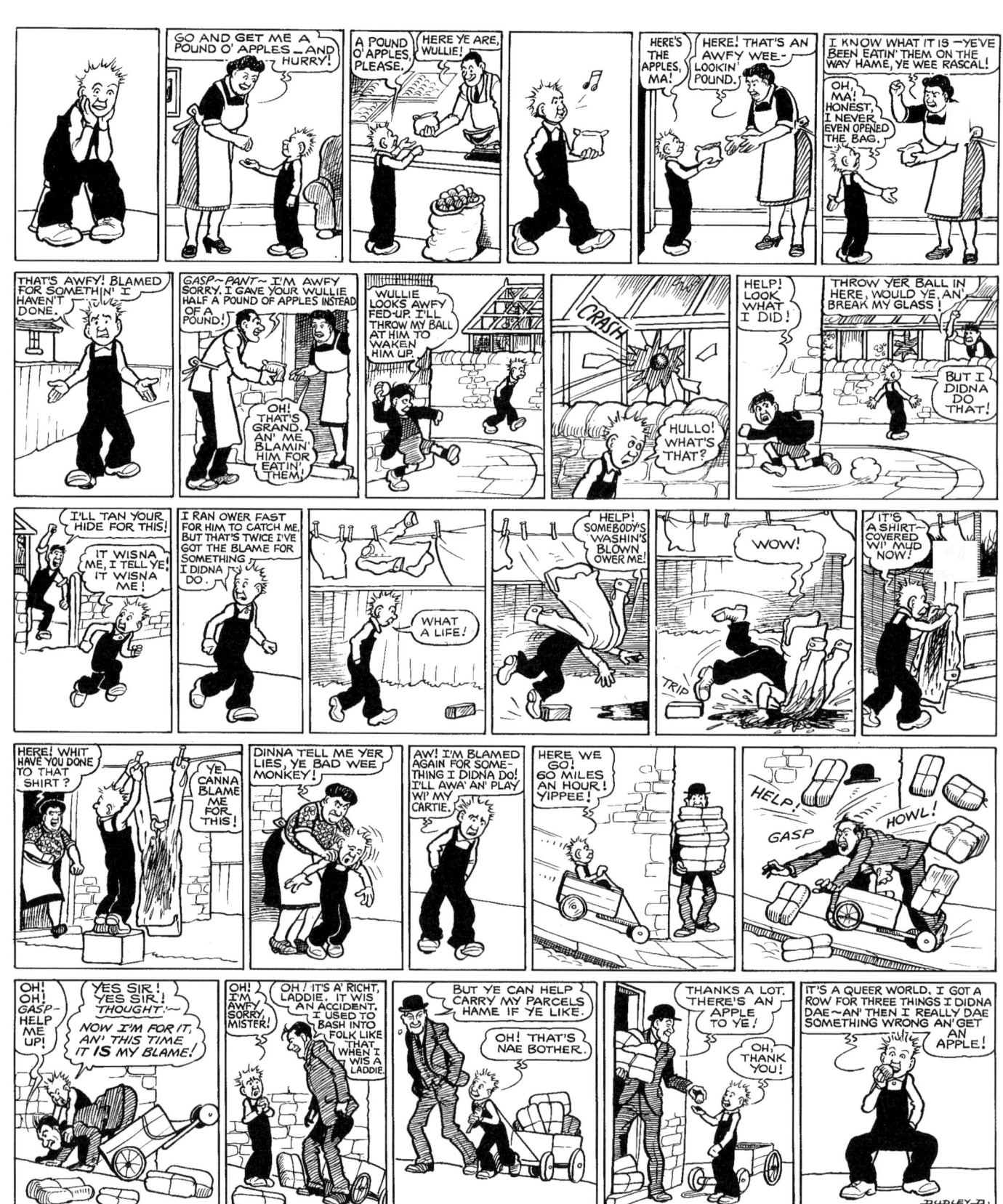

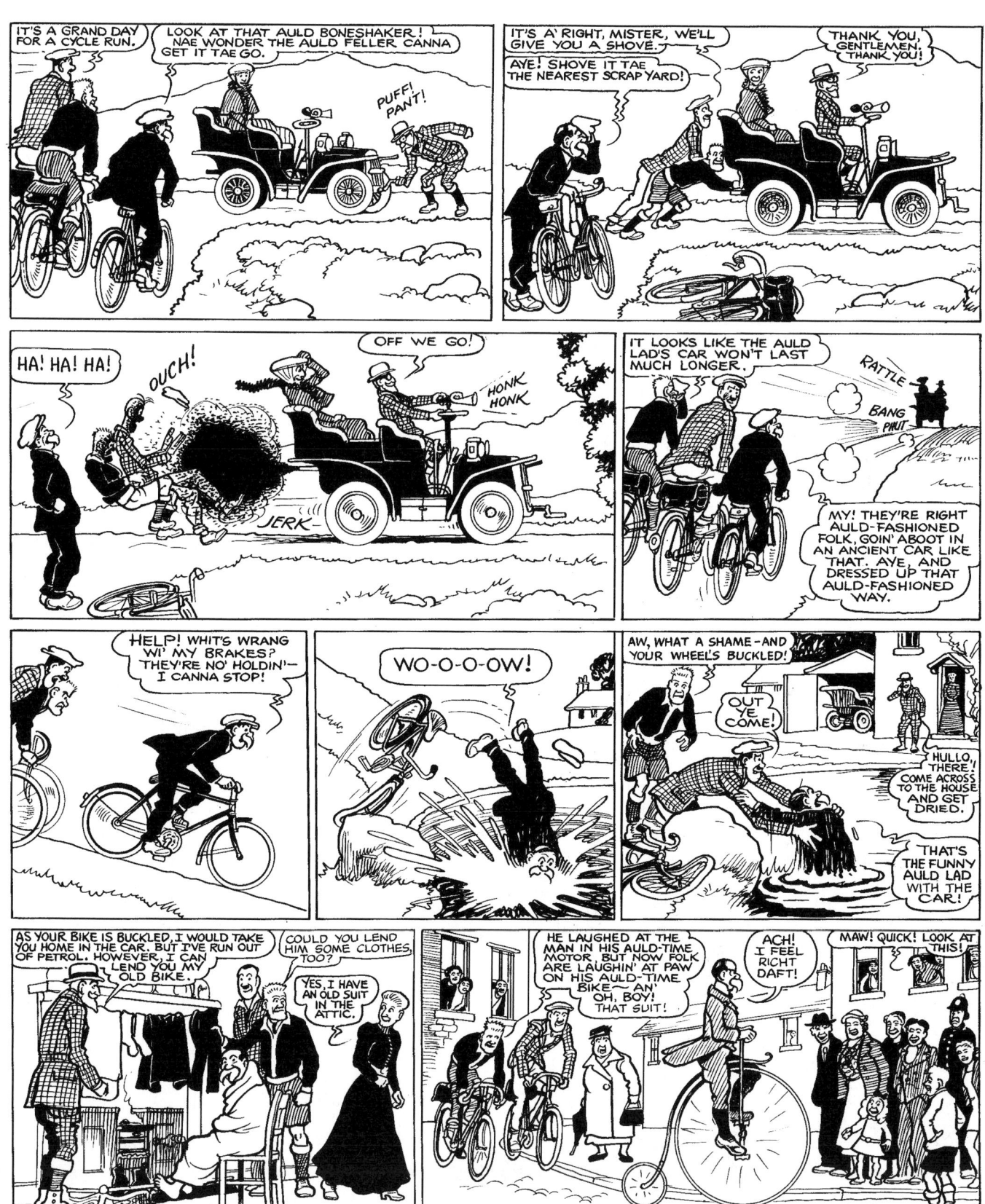

The Sunday Post 13th June 1954

The Sunday Post 19th September 1954

The Sunday Post 18th July 1954

114

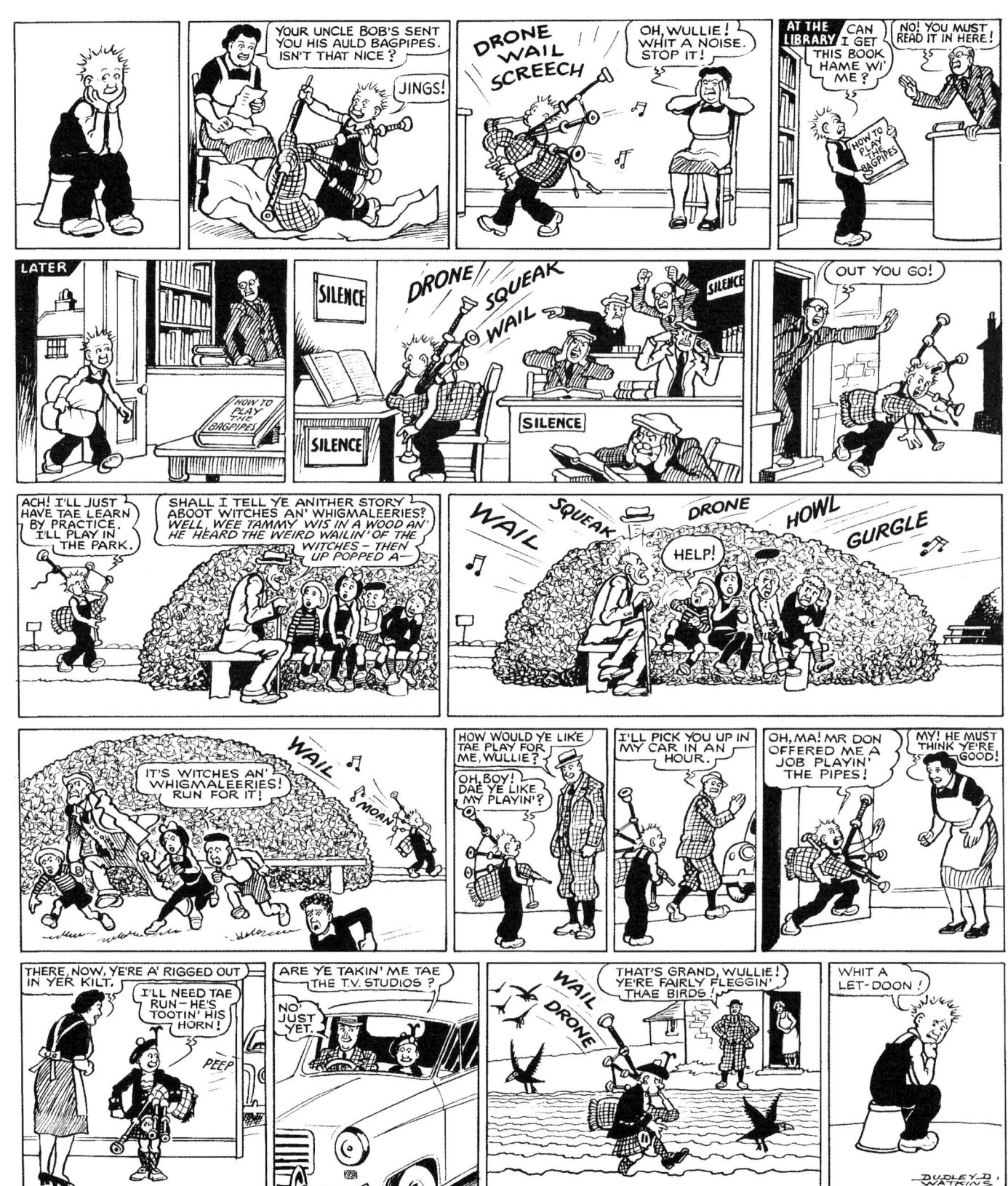

The Sunday Post 3rd October 1954

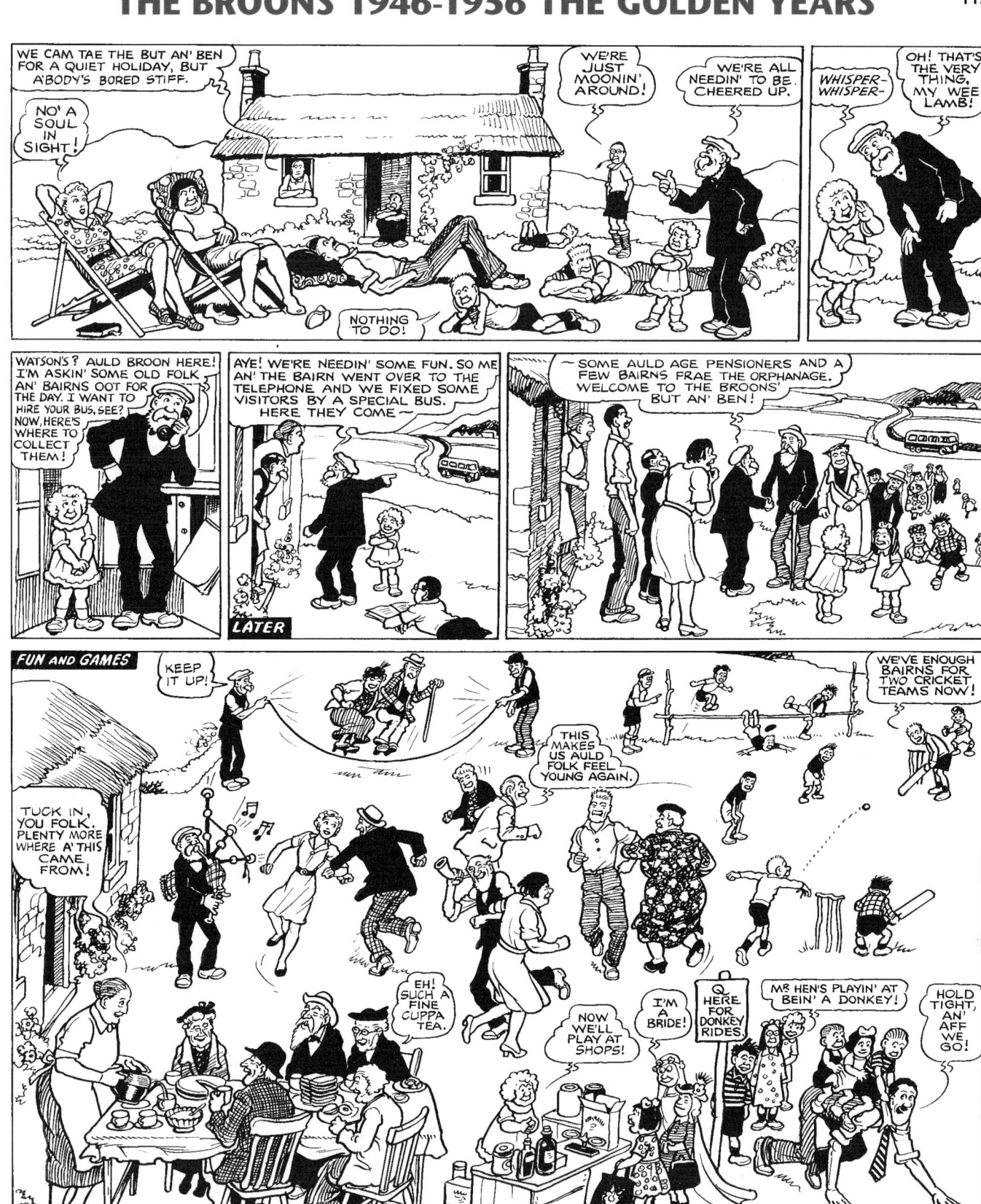

The Sunday Post 1st August 1954

The Sunday Post 5th December 1954

The Sunday Post 15th August 1954

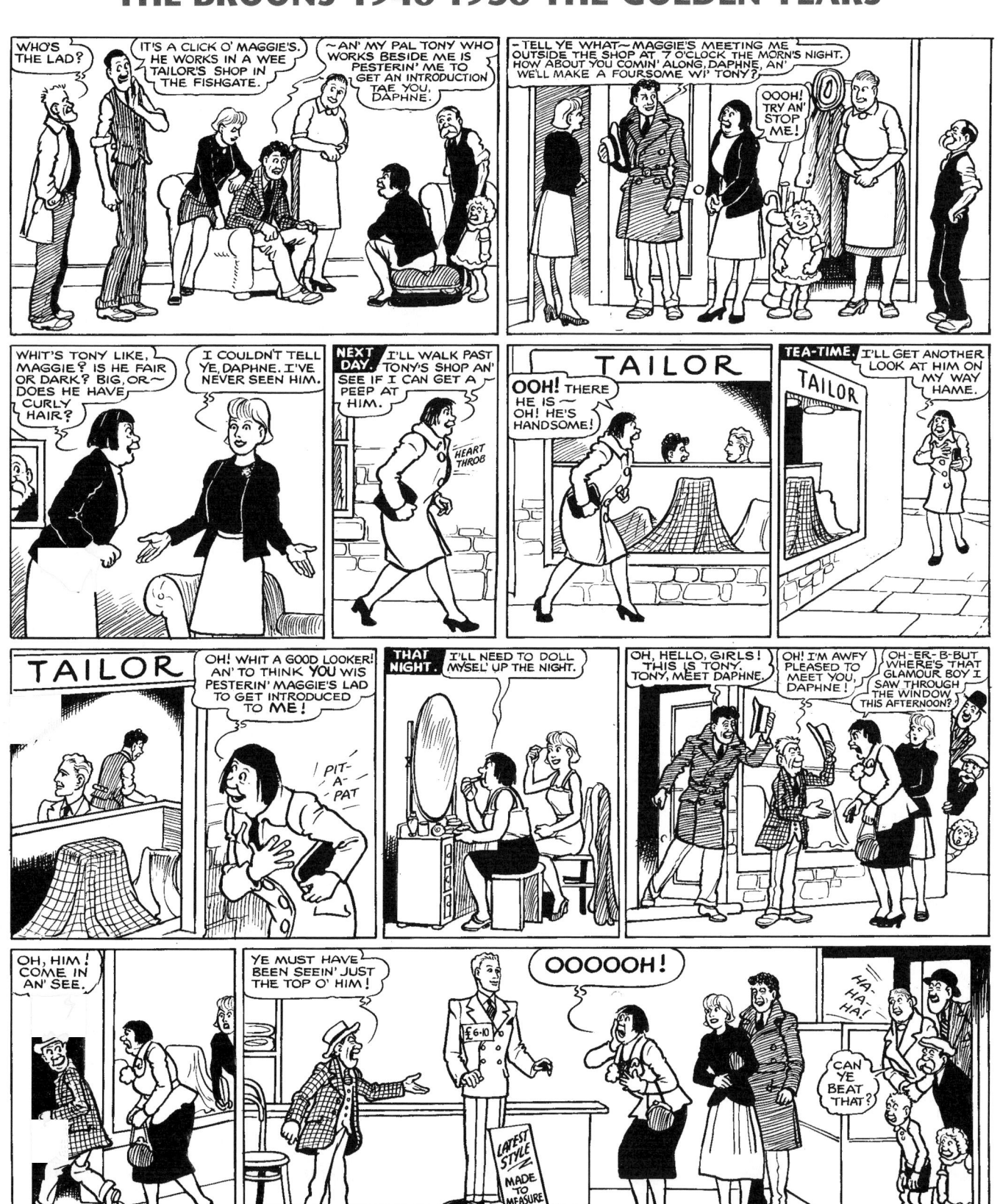

The Sunday Post 21st November 1954

1955

Dressmaking and knitting were popular pastimes for many women — and Daphne liked to think of herself as the seamstress of Number 10. The problem was, the finished outfits never seemed to look as good on Daph as they did on the models. However, that wouldn't put her off and she loved to look through magazines such as "My Weekly" for the latest up-to-the-minute styles.

A HAPPY NEW YEAR TO ALL OUR

MY WEEKLY

The Paper For Every Woman
On Sale Every Tuesday

POODLE COAT
— Quick To Knit
Smart To Wear

STORIES
by
Lynn Bretton
Joan G...
Ma...

PRICE 3P

Stories by DOROTHY RIVERS : MARGARET BAUMANN
AUDRIE MANLEY-TUCKER : ELIZABETH HARDING

MY WEEKLY

The Paper For Every Woman
On Sale Every Tuesday

2 CHARMING STYLES To Knit

INSTRUCTIONS INSIDE

OFFERED THIS WEEK
A Lillie London Pattern that makes
3 DRESSES!
...EB 5 1955   PRICE 3D

"My Weekly" also contained many recipes to tempt the readers and stories to cheer them up when their efforts — at cooking or dressmaking — left them feeling down-in-the-dumps. Dramas like "The Man She'll Never Marry!" proved perfect antidotes to a frustrating day with needles, thread or sauce pan!

Some events from 1955...
Disneyland opened in July in Anaheim, California.
ITV, Britain's first commercial television station, was launched.
McDonald's fast-food chain was formed.
Bill Haley and the Comets reached Number One with "Rock Around The Clock".
Winston Churchill resigned as Prime Minister, and was replaced by Anthony Eden.

The Sunday Post 6th February 1955

The Sunday Post 9th January 1955

The Sunday Post 6th March 1955

The Sunday Post 6th March 1955

The Sunday Post 17th April 1955

The Sunday Post 3rd April 1955

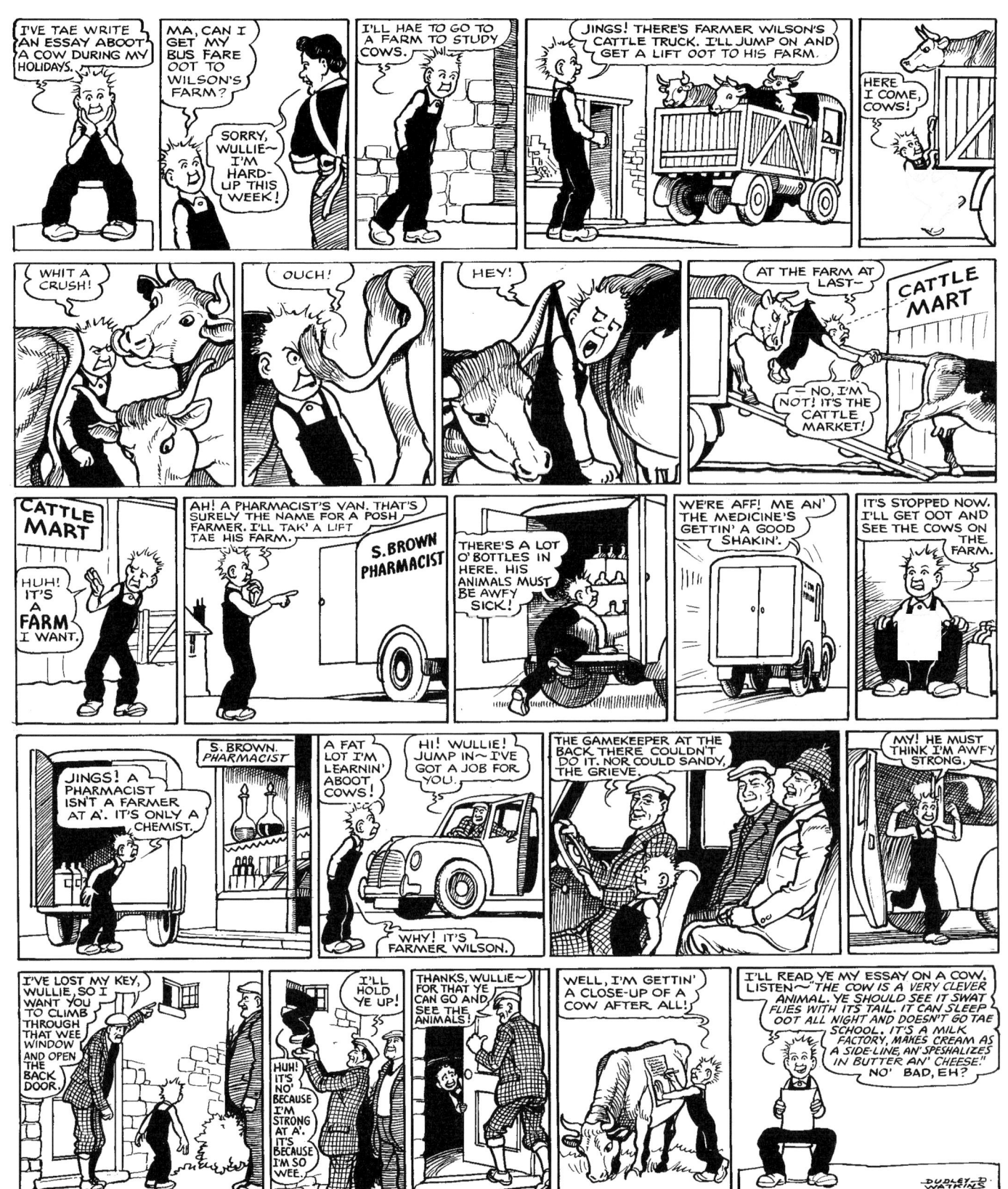

The Sunday Post 28th August 1955

The Sunday Post 8th May 1955

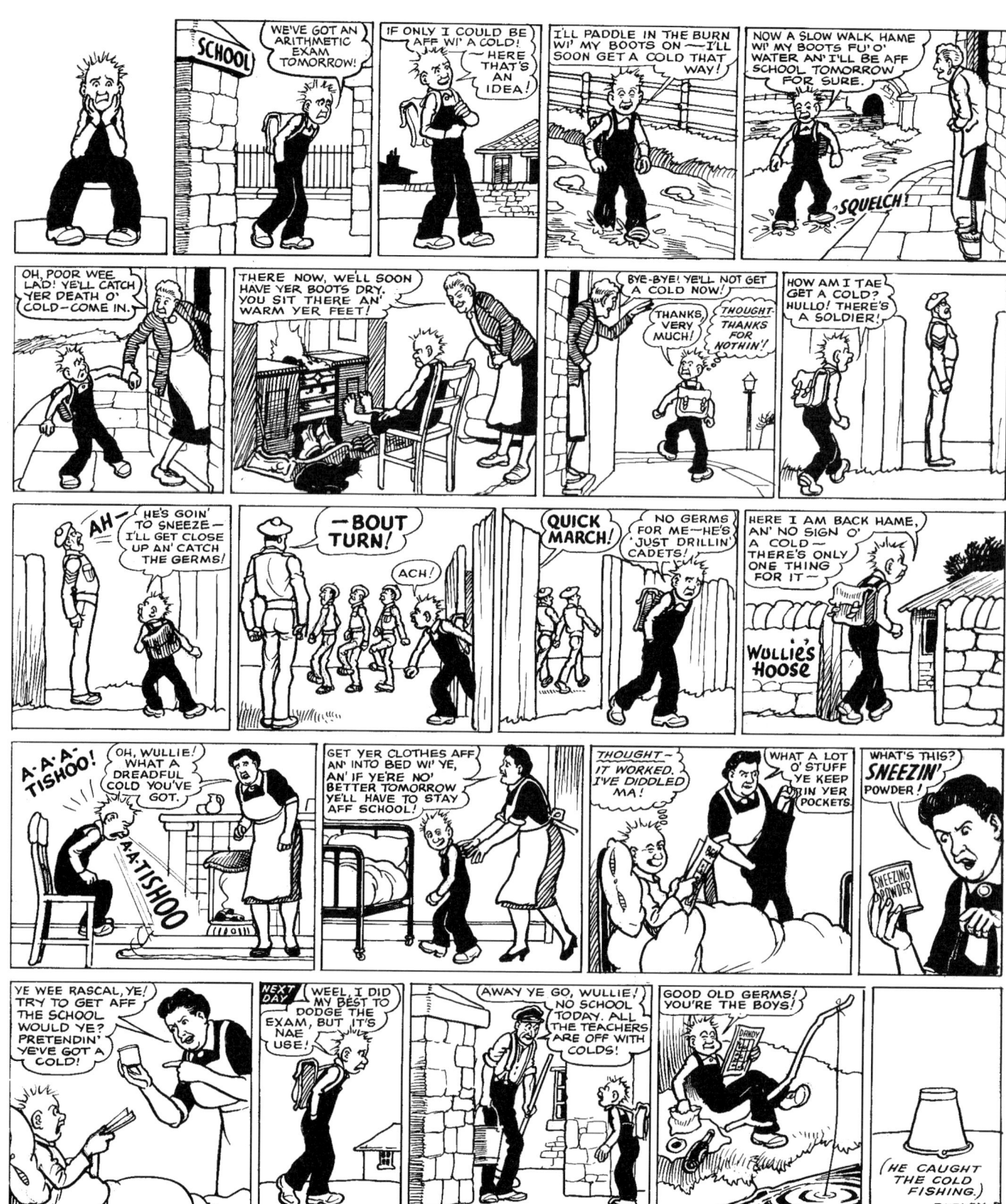

The Sunday Post 2nd October 1955

The Sunday Post 31st July 1955

The Sunday Post 13th November 1955

The Sunday Post 23rd October 1955

1956

If you were to ask Hen any question about films or film stars, ninety-nine times out of a hundred he would give you the right answer. The cinema was a very popular source of entertainment with young and old, and there would usually be long queues when a brand new film was screened. Hen would also spend time collecting any information he could about Hollywood film stars, often through cuttings from his favourite paper — "The Weekly News".

THE WEEKLY NEWS

No. 5248 SATURDAY, JANUARY 14, 1956. Price 3d.

Paging All Readers

WITH THIS WEEK'S EXTRA SPECIALS...

PAGE 6
"TERROR MOUNTAIN"
the start of a great new serial
by Victor Canning

PAGE 2
The fabulous story of JOSEPHINE BAKER
the w
who m
whol

THE WEEKLY NEWS

No. 5252 SATURDAY, FEBRUARY 11, 1956. Price 3d.

THESE FOOLISH THINGS
I GET A KICK OUT OF YOU
Someone To Watch Over Me

ALL THE WORDS OF THESE FAMOUS

Sinatra Song Hits

INSIDE FOR YOU
with another great instalment of
"ALL ABOUT FRANKIE"

MOST Beau
IN THE WOR

and that's also the title of Gina Lollo-brigida's latest film, made in Italy. In it Gina realises a lifelong ambition—to ride a cycle! In one scene it was suddenly decided to have Gina riding a bicycle down a woodland two hours in which to learn. She did terwards was seen cycling

ALL Hollywood is wondering if GRACE KELLY, Princess Rainier of Monaco-to-be, can now complete a big film "hat-trick." In her last two films for Paramount, "The Country Girl" and "To Catch A Thief," she has collected an Oscar and a Royal Command accolade. Now filming "The Swan," Grace has high hopes.

He soon lea

This weekly paper was packed with news and interviews with stars of the silver screen. There were also regular features on the Queen and members of Royal families — both home and abroad. Hen could read it all and dream that one day he TOO would be a film star — even although Joe joked that the nearest he'd get to stars would be at night, looking through a telescope!

Some events from 1956...
Real Madrid won the first European Cup by defeating Stade de Reims 4-3.
Actress Grace Kelly married Prince Rainier of Monaco.
The Suez Crisis, involving Britain, France, Israel and Egypt, began.
The first Eurovision Song Contest was broadcast from Lugano, Switzerland, and was won by the host country.
The submarine transatlantic telephone link was opened.

The Sunday Post 15th January 1956

The Sunday Post 1st January 1956

OOR WULLIE 1946-1956 THE GOLDEN YEARS

The Sunday Post 22nd January 1956

The Sunday Post 19th February 1956

The Sunday Post 26th February 1956

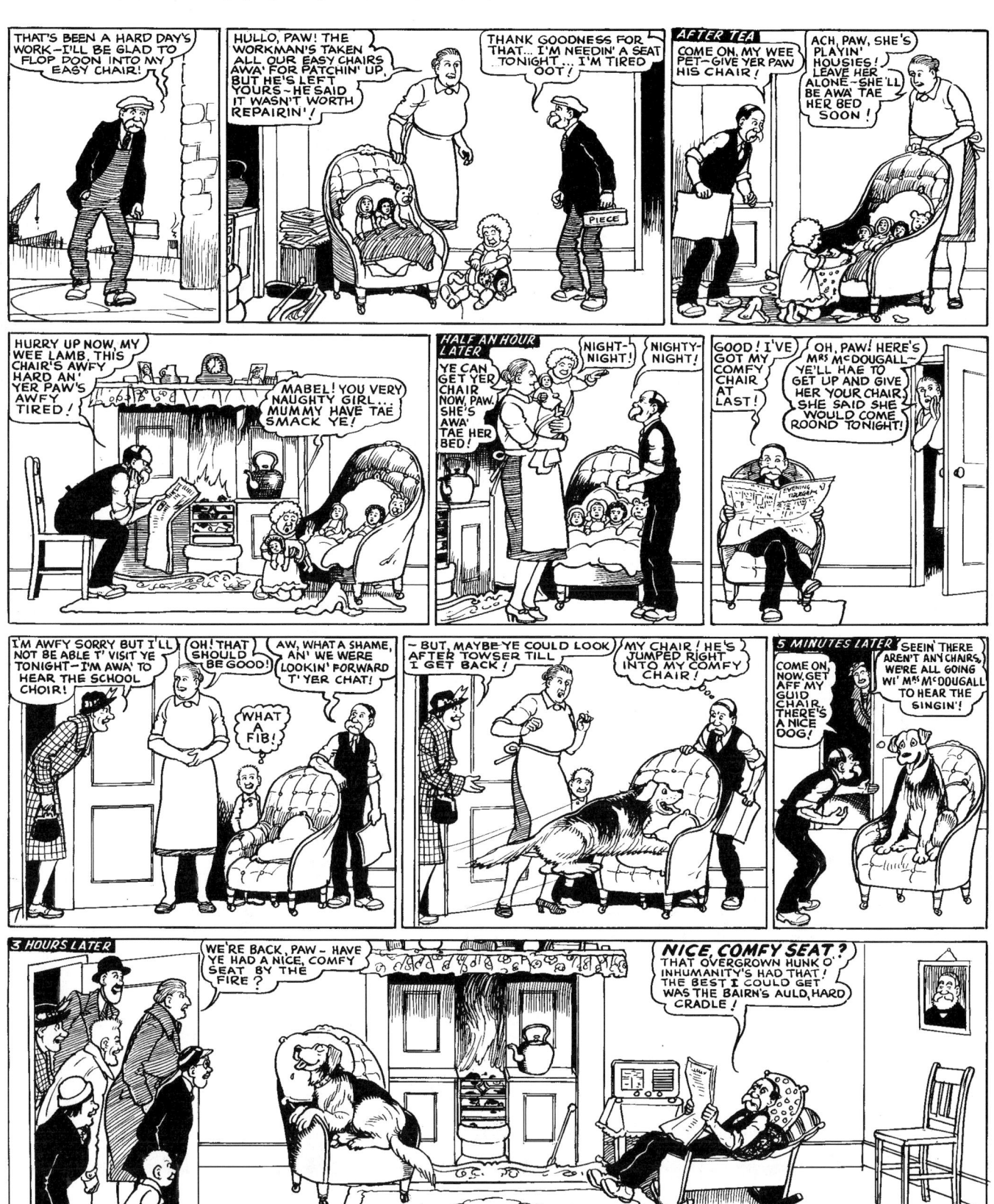

The Sunday Post 4th March 1956